Address Book

A Complete Everyday Companion

"What's in a name? That which we call a rose
By any other name would smell as sweet."

Shakespeare (Romeo & Juliet)

A Robert Frederick Gift Book

Address Book

A Complete Everyday Companion

INDEX

INDEX

Personal Notes

Name ....

Address ....

Tel.: Home ....

      Business ....

      Car ....

In Case of Emergency

Contact ....

Telephone No. ....

Blood Group ....

Known Allergies ....

❖ Useful Telephone Numbers

Accountant	Optician ....
Airport	Plumber ....
Bank	Railway Station ....
Building Society	Solicitor ....
Club	Taxi/Car Hire ....
Dentist	Travel Agent ....
Doctor	Vet ....
Electrician	Water ....
Gas	Other ....

❖ Useful Information

National Insurance No.	Car Key No. ....
Passport No.	Car Insurance Policy No. ....
Driving Licence No.	Renewal Date ....
Credit Card No.s	AA/RAC Membership No. ....

❖ Notes

....

....

....

USEFUL TELEPHONE NUMBERS

Name .... ☎ ....

Name .... ☎ ....

Name .... ☎ ....

Name .... ☎ ....

Name .... ☎ ....

Name .... ☎ ....

Name .... ☎ ....

Name .... ☎ ....

Name .... ☎ ....

Name .... ☎ ....

Name .... ☎ ....

Name .... ☎ ....

Name .... ☎ ....

Name .... ☎ ....

Name .... ☎ ....

Name .... ☎ ....

Name .... ☎ ....

Name .... ☎ ....

Name .... ☎ ....

Name .... ☎ ....

Name .... ☎ ....

Name .... ☎ ....

Name .... ☎ ....

THINGS TO REMEMBER

Use this space to note down renewal dates for Television Licence, Road Tax, MOT, Insurance policies etc.

BIRTH SIGNS

ARIES (March 21-April 20)
Fiery First Sign
Symbol: The Ram
Ruling Planet: Mars
Birthstone: Diamond
Flower: Sweet Pea
Colours: Fiery Red, Orange
Numbers: Seven, Six
Day: Tuesday

TAURUS (April 21-May 21)
Earthy Second Sign
Symbol: The Bull
Ruling Planet: Venus
Birthstone: Emerald
Flower: Lily of the Valley
Colours: Natural colours
Numbers: One, Nine
Day: Friday

GEMINI (May 22-June 21)
Airy Third Sign
Symbol: The Twins
Ruling Planet: Mercury
Birthstone: Agate
Flower: Rose
Colours: Sky Blue, Black
Numbers: Three, Four
Day: Wednesday

CANCER (June 22-July 22)
Watery Fourth Sign
Symbol: Crab, Moon
Ruling Planet: The Moon
Birthstone: Moonstone, Pearl
Flower: Larkspur
Colours: Silver, Sea Green
Numbers: Eight, Three
Day: Friday

LEO (July 23-August 23)
Fiery & Fixed Fifth Sign
Symbol: The Sun, The Lion
Ruling Planet: The Sun
Birthstone: Sardonyx
Flower: Gladioli
Colours: Gold, Fiery Shades
Numbers: Five, Nine
Day: Sunday

VIRGO (August 24-Sept. 22)
Earthy & Adaptable Sixth Sign
Symbol: Fertility Goddess
Ruling Planet: Mercury
Birthstone: Sapphire
Flower: Aster
Colours: Natural, Warm
Numbers: Eight, Four
Day: Wednesday

LIBRA (Sept. 23-Oct. 23)
Airy Sociable Seventh Sign
Symbol: The Scales
Ruling Plant: Venus
Birthstone: Opal
Flower: Calendula
Colour: Peacock Blue
Numbers: Six, Nine
Day: Friday

SCORPIO (Oct. 24-Nov. 22)
Watery Eighth Sign
Symbol: The Scorpion
Ruling Planet: Mars
Birthstone: Topaz
Flower: Chrysanthemum
Colours: Dark Water Shades
Numbers: Three, Five
Day: Tuesday

SAGITTARIUS (Nov. 23-Dec. 23)
Fiery, Adaptable Ninth Sign
Symbol: The Archer
Ruling Planet: Jupiter
Birthstone: Turquoise
Flower: Narcissus
Colours: Fiery Reds
Numbers: Nine
Day: Thursday

CAPRICORN (Dec. 24-Jan. 20)
Earthy Tenth Sign
Symbol: The Goat
Ruling Planet: Saturn
Birthstone: Garnet
Flower: Carnation
Colours: Restrained to Dark
Numbers: Seven, Three
Day: Saturday

AQUARIUS (Jan. 21-Feb. 18)
Airy, Stubborn Eleventh Sign
Symbol: Water Carrier
Ruling Planet: Uranus
Birthstone: Amethyst
Flower: Violet
Colours; Wild, Way Out
Numbers: Eight, Four
Day: Wednesday

PISCES (Feb.19-March 20)
Watery, Compromising Twelfth Sign
Symbol: Two Fish
Ruling Planet: Neptune
Birthstone: Bloodstone
Flower: Jonquil
Colours: Violet, Oceanic
Numbers: Five, Eight
Day: Friday

BIRTHDAYS

Spouse ....

....

Children .... Other Family ....

....

....

....

....

Grandchildren ....

....

.... Friends

....

....

....

....

....

....

....

Mother ....

Father .... Miscellaneous

Mother-in-law ....

Father-in-law ....

Brothers & Sisters ....

....

....

....

....

ANNIVERSARIES

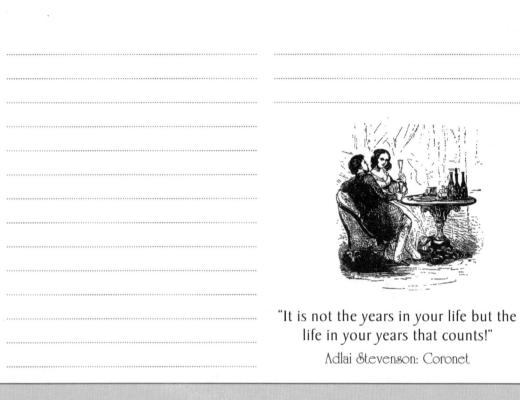

"It is not the years in your life but the
life in your years that counts!"

Adlai Stevenson: Coronet

~ WEDDING ANNIVERSARIES ~

First	Paper			Thirtieth	Pearl
Second	Cotton	Tenth	Tin	Thirty-fifth	Coral
Third	Leather	Eleventh	Steel	Forty-fifth	Sapphire
Fourth	Fruit, Flowers	Twelfth	Silk, Linen	Fortieth	Ruby
Fifth	Wood	Thirteenth	Lace	Fiftieth	Gold
Sixth	Sugar, Iron	Fourteenth	Ivory	Fifty-fifth	Emerald
Seventh	Wool, Copper	Fifteenth	Crystal	Sixtieth	Diamond
Eighth	Bronze, Pottery	Twentieth	China	Seventieth	Platinum
Ninth	Pottery, Willow	Twenty-fifth	Silver	Seventy-fifth	Diamond

SPECIAL OCCASIONS

Occasion .... Date ....

Occasion .... Date ....

Occasion .... Date ....

Occasion .... Date ....

Occasion .... Date ....

Occasion .... Date ....

Occasion .... Date ....

Occasion .... Date ....

Occasion .... Date ....

Occasion .... Date ....

Occasion .... Date ....

Occasion .... Date ....

Occasion .... Date ....

"All who joy would win
Must share it, -
Happiness was born a
Twin."

Byron: Don Juan

HELPLINES

AA ALCOHOLICS ANONYMOUS
071-352 3001

11 Radcliff Gardens, London SW10 9BG
Helpline 10am-10pm   24hour answer phone service

A fellowship of men and women who share their experience with each other that they may solve their common problem and help others to recover from alcoholism. The only requirement for membership is an honest desire to stop. Publications are available.

AGE CONCERN
081-679 8000

Astral House, 1268 London Road, London SW16 4ER

Provides information and advice to older people and their carers and runs public education campaigns to raise awareness of issues relating to older people.
Send SAE for more information.

AL-ANON
071-403 0888 (24-hour)

61 Great Dover Street, London SE1 4YF

Al-Anon helps families of problem drinkers. Alateen helps teenagers (aged 12-20) who have been, or who are, affected by an alcoholic relative.

ARTHRITIS CARE
18-20 Stephenson Way, London NW1 2HD

Works with people of all ages with arthritis, improving their quality of life and raising awareness in the public and in policy-makers of this serious chronic and disabling disease. There are 550 branches offering welfare advice and there is also a special section for young people.

BACUP (BRITISH ASSOC. OF CANCER UNITED PATIENTS)
071-608 1661

0800-181199 (Freephone for callers outside the 071 area)
121-123 Charterhouse Street, London EC1M 6AA

Provides a free, confidential information and support service to cancer patients and their families and friends by telephone and letter, on all types of cancer and produces a newspaper, leaflets and booklets.

BREAK
0263-823170

20 Hooks Hill Road, Sheringham, Norfolk NR26 8NL

Aims to provide holidays, respite and care for profoundly handicapped children and adults, and families with special needs. Publications are available.

BRITISH ASSOCIATION FOR COUNSELLING
0788-578328

1 Regent Place, Rugby CV21 2PJ

Provides informed comment on many current issues - members have experience of a wide range of counselling practice in settings such as drug abuse, unemployment, alcoholism, relationships, bereavement and AIDS/HIV. Send a large SAE for a list of counsellors in your locality.

BRITISH DIABETIC ASSOCIATION
071-323 1531

(Head Office) 10 Queen Anne St, London W1M 0BD

The Association provides advice, information and support for people with diabetes including a bi-monthly magazine "Balance". With over 400 branches providing local support, new members are welcome. For further information and the Help Line contact Head Office.

BRITISH EPILEPSY ASSOCIATION
0532-439393 (info) 0345-089599 (helpline)

Anstey House, 40 Hanover Square, Leeds LS3 1BE

The association provides advice, information and support for people with epilepsy. "Action for Epilepsy" is a national network for self-help local groups. Send SAE for more information.

EVERYDAY THOUGHTS
for everyday living

"They are able because they think
they are able."

Virgil

"Natural ability without education has
oftener raised men to glory and virtue,
than education without natural ability."

Cicero

"Our hours in love have wings;
in absence crutches."

Colley Cibber

"Absence diminishes moderate
passions and increases great ones,
as the wind extinguishes tapers and
adds fury to fire."

La Rochefoucauld

"He knows not his own strength that
hath not met adversity."

Ben Jonson

A

Name

✉

☎

Name

✉

☎

Name

✉

☎

Name

✉

☎

Name

✉

☎

Name

✉

☎

Name

✉

☎

☎ HELPLINES ☎

BRITISH MIGRAINE ASSOCIATION
09323-52468
178a High Road, Byfleet, West Byfleet, Surrey KT14 7ED

The Association encourages migraine sufferers to support research into the causes and alleviation of migraine. It offers reassurance and understanding and keeps all members informed of progress in research and the latest treatments.

BROOK ADVISORY CENTRES
071-708-1234
153a East Street, London SE17 2SD

The Centres help young people with confidential contraceptive advice and supplies, pregnancy testing, and counselling for sexual and emotional problems and unwanted pregnancies. Young people can be sure of sympathetic and confidential advice and practical help. Send SAE for publications.

CARERS NATIONAL ASSOCIATION
071-724 7776
29 Chilworth Mews, London W2 3RG

Aims to help anyone whose life is in some way restricted because of the need to take responsibility for the care of a person who is handicapped, or whose health is impaired by sickness or old age. Regular newsletters, information and an advice service are available.

CHILDLINE
0800-1111 (freephone)
2nd Floor, Royal Mail Building, Studd Street, London N1 0QW

ChildLine is the free, national helpline for children and young people in trouble or danger. It provides a confidential telephone counselling service 24 hours a day for any child with any problem. Trained counsellors listen, comfort and protect. Publications are available.

COT DEATH HELPLINE
071-235 1721 (24 hour)
The Foundation for the Study of Infant Deaths
35 Belgrave Square, London SW1X 8QB

The helpline will respond at any time to bereaved cot death families. There will be someone to listen, to ask about the baby and what happened, to give explanations where possible and offer information, advice and reassurance.

CRUSE (BEREAVEMENT CARE)
081-940 4818
126 Sheen Road, Richmond, Surrey TW9 1UR

185 branches offering a service of counselling, advice and opportunities for social contact to all bereaved people. Publications are available.

CRY-SIS
071-404 5011
Cry-sis BM, London WC1N 3XX

CRY-SIS provides emotional support and practical advice to parents of babies who cry incessantly and older children with problems such as temper tantrums. Activities include a national network of self-help groups; putting mothers in touch with others with similar problems. Publications are available.

DEPRESSIVES ANONYMOUS
0482-860619
36 Chestnut Avenue, Beverley, North Humberside HU17 9QU

Encouragement and support for sufferers and relatives, through fellowship. There is a newsletter and penfriend scheme, small local groups and regular open meetings. Send SAE or phone for information, not counselling.

DIAL UK
0302-310123
Park Lodge, St Catherine's Hospital, Tickhill Rd, Balby, Doncaster, S Yorks DN4 8QN

Free, impartial and confidential service of advice, information and counselling on all aspects of disability, to disabled people and carers. Publications are available.

EVERYDAY THOUGHTS
for everyday living

"There is nothing which we receive
with so much reluctance as advice."

Joseph Addison

"Age only matters when one is aging.
Now that I have arrived at a great age.
I might just as well be twenty."

Picasso

"Aim at the sun, and you may not
reach it; but your arrow will fly far
higher than if aimed at an object on a
level with yourself."

J Hawes

"He that is slow to anger is better than
the mighty; and he that ruleth his spirit
than he that taketh a city."

Proverbs 16:32

"The only way to get the best of an
argument is to avoid it."

Dale Carnegie

A

Name
✉

☎
Name
✉

☎
Name
✉

☎
Name
✉

☎
Name
✉

☎
Name
✉

☎
Name
✉

☎

DYSLEXIA INSTITUTE
0784-463851

133 Gresham Road, Staines, Middx TW18 2AJ

Offers information and advice for parents, expert examination of difficulties and specialist teaching. Teaching, assessment and training centres have been established around the country. Publications are available.

EATING DISORDER ASSOCIATION
0603-621 414

Sackville Place, 44 Magdalen St, Norfolk NR3 1JU
0603-765 050 (Mon-Wed 4-6pm) Youth Helpline (under 18's)

EDA offers help with anorexia and bulimia through helplines, information about self-help groups, counsellors and treatment throughout UK. Send large SAE for more information.

ERIC (ENURESIS RESOURCE AND INFORMATION CENTRE)
0272-264920

65 St Michael's Hill, Bristol BS2 8DZ

ERIC aims to improve the awareness of bed wetting and identify the related problems, offering information for both parents and professionals. Publications are available.

FAIR (FAMILY ACTION INFORMATION AND RESCUE)
081-539 3940

BCM Box 3535, PO Box 12, London WC1N 3XX

FAIR counsel and work with those involved with extremist religious cults, their families and friends. Information is provided to alert government departments, the media, and public bodies to the dangers. Publications are available.

GAMBLERS ANONYMOUS & GAM-ANON
081-741 4181

PO Box 88, London SW10 0EU

Gamblers Anonymous are a fellowship of men and women who have joined together in self-help counselling groups to redress the damage caused by gambling. Gam-Anon offers friendship, practical help, comfort and understanding to parents, husbands and wives of compulsive gamblers. Send SAE for literature.

GINGERBREAD
071-240 0953

35 Wellington Street, London WC2E 7BN

Practical help for lone parents and their children via a national network of local self-help groups, with over 300 local groups meeting regularly. Social activities are arranged for parents and children; some groups run day-care schemes and other special projects. Advice line open between 2-5pm. Publications are available.

HOSPICE INFORMATION SERVICE
081-778 9252

St Christopher's Hospice, 51-59 Lawrie Park Rd, Sydenham, London SE26 6DZ

The Hospice Information Service publishes a directory which provides details of hospices, home care teams and hospital support teams throughout the UK. Write or telephone for information.

KIDSCAPE (CAMPAIGN FOR CHILDREN'S SAFETY)
071-730 3300

152 Buckingham Palace Rd, London SW1W 9TR

Kidscape campaigns for children's safety. It deals with bullying, getting lost, stranger danger and threats of abuse from known adults. Send large SAE for free parents' guides.

NAC (NATIONAL ASSOCIATION FOR THE CHILDLESS)
021-359 7359

Birmingham Settlement, 318 Summer Lane, Birmingham B19 3RL

NAC provides information on all aspects of infertility and alternative routes to parenthood. A confidential helpline provides counselling and support at times of crisis to those with fertility problems. Send SAE for more information.

EVERYDAY THOUGHTS
for everyday living

"Every baby born into the world is a finer one than the last."

Charles Dickens: Nicholas Nickleby

"A baby is an angel whose wings decrease as his legs increase."

French Proverb

" A beautiful face is of all spectacles the most beautiful."

Jean De La Bruyère

"Achieving starts with believing."

Author Unidentified

"A man lives by believing something: not by debating and arguing about many things."

Thomas Carlyle

B

Name

✉

☎

Name

✉

☎

Name

✉

☎

Name

✉

☎

Name

✉

☎

Name

✉

☎

☎ HELPLINES ☎

NACAB
National Association of Citizens' Advice Bureaux
115-123 Pentonville Road, London N1 9LZ

Has branches throughout the UK, is independent and provides free, confidential, impartial advice to everybody regardless of race, gender, sexuality or disability. Each branch is listed in the local phone book under 'C' or call Directory Enquiries.

NAPS (National Assoc. for Premenstrual Syndrome)
0227-763133
PO Box 72, Sevenoaks, Kent TN13 1XQ

Offers advice whilst providing a greater awareness of Premenstrual Syndrome combined with research. Campaigns for its recognition by all members of the medical profession. Publications are available.

National Association of Widows
021-643 8348
54-57 Allison Street, Digbeth, Birmingham B5 5TH

Advice, information and friendly support to all widows. A specialist advice service is available from the Association's head office; branches throughout the country provide a supportive social role.

National Asthma Campaign
071-226 2260
Providence House, Providence Place, London N1 0NT

Offers help and advice for asthmatics to understand and control their condition so that they may live healthier and more active lives. Publications are available.

National Back Pain Association
081-977 5474
31-33 Park Road, Teddington TW11 0AB

Publishes leaflets on causes and treatment of back pain to educate people to use their bodies properly.

National Council for One Parent Families
071-267 1361
255 Kentish Town Road, London NW5 2LX

Aims to improve the social position of one parent families, offering an information service and re-employment training. It is campaigning to improve provision for lone parents and their children. Publications are available.

National Debtline
021-359 8501
Birmingham Settlement, 318 Summer Lane, Birmingham B19 3RL

The Helpline provides expert advice for people in debt, their options and their legal rights - dealing with all debts including mortgage and rent arrears. There is a free information pack for callers.

National Eczema Society
071-388 4097
4 Tavistock Place, London WC1H 9RA

Information for people with eczema and their carers. Send a large SAE for free literature giving advice on the general management of eczema.

National Listening Library
071-407 9417
12 Lant St, London SE1 1QH

The Library provides a postal lending service of literature recorded on cassettes for the benefit of physically and mentally handicapped adults and children who are unable to read in the conventional way. Dyslexics are also eligible.

EVERYDAY THOUGHTS
for everyday living

"Burdens become light when
cheerfully borne."

Ovid

"Whenever you see a successful
business, someone once made a
courageous decision."

Peter Drucker

"To business that we love we rise
betime,
And go to't with delight."

Shakespeare: Anthony and Cleopatra

"Few people do business well who do
nothing else."

Lord Chesterfield

"The busier we are, the more acutely
we feel that we live, the more
conscious we are of life."

Immanuel Kant

Addresses • Addresses • Addresses • Addresses • Addresses • Addresses • Addresses

𝕭

Name
✉

☎
Name
✉

☎
Name
✉

☎
Name
✉

☎
Name
✉

☎
Name
✉

☎

NATIONAL OSTEOPOROSIS SOCIETY
07614-32472

PO Box 10, Radstock, Bath, Avon BA3 3YB

The Society publishes useful results of research into Osteoporosis. Specialist advice is given by phone or letter and there are local groups. Send SAE for more information.

PARENTLINE
0268-757077

(Organisations For Parents Under Stress)
Rayfa House, 57 Hart Road, Thundersley, Essex SS7 3PD

A network of telephone helplines for parents who are experiencing problems with their children. Callers may remain anonymous. Look for the number in local directory or ring the national office for information.

QUIT
071-487 3000 (Smokers Quitline)

National Society of Non-Smokers
102 Gloucester Place, London, W1H 3DA.

Offers help for smokers trying to give up. QUIT runs Stop Smoking groups for the general public and in-house for the workplace. Telephone counselling is offered through 'Smokers' Quitline'. Send SAE for publications.

RELATE (NATIONAL MARRIAGE GUIDANCE)
0788-573241

Herbert Gray College, Little Church Street,
Rugby, Warwicks CV21 3AP

160 local Relate centres (marriage guidance councils), undertake education in personal relationships and counselling for those seeking help in marriage, family relationships and sexual problems.

RELEASE
071-729 9904 (10am-6pm) 071-603 8654 (24 hour)

388 Old Street, London EC1V 9LT

Offers advice and referral on criminal legal problems, illegal & prescribed drug counselling and referral service. 24hr emergency helpline in cases of arrest.

RNID
0345-090210 (Tinnitus Helpline)

RNID, Pelham Court, Pelham Rd, Nottingham NG5 4P

This is a national telephone helpline offering advice, information and support to all people with Tinnitus (noises in the ear or head). Calls are charged at local rate Mon-Fri 10am-3pm.

SALVATION ARMY
071-383 4230

105-109 Judd St, Kings Cross, London WC1H 9TS

Trained counsellors listen and advise on a wide spectrum of problems. Callers may be referred to local counsellors. The service is open to anyone, anywhere, irrespective of religion.

SAMARITANS

Samaritans offer a 24-hour, absolutely confidential service for people who are in despair, many of whom feel suicidal. Samaritans are ordinary people from all walks of life who devote part of their spare time to helping ordinary people in distress. Carefully selected, they work under the guidance of a volunteer director who has the advice of a consultant psychiatrist. Ring, write or visit your nearest branch, listed in the local phone book under 'S'.

SANDS (STILLBIRTH AND NEONATAL DEATH SOCIETY)
071-436 5881

28 Portland Place, London W1N 4DE

Offers support through self-help groups and befriending to parents bereaved through pregnancy loss, still birth or neonatal death. The Society produces a newsletter and information leaflets, a Helpline service during normal office hours plus 24hr answer phone service.

EVERYDAY THOUGHTS
for everyday living

"Challenges can be stepping stones or stumbling blocks. It's just a matter of how you view them."

Author Unidentified

"Wondrous is the strength of cheerfulness, and its power of endurance - the cheerful man will do more in the same time, will do it better, will persevere in it longer than the sad or sullen."

Thomas Carlyle

"Of cheerfulness, or a good temper - the more it is spent, the more of it remains."

Ralph Waldo Emmerson

"Children are the true connoisseurs. What's precious to them has no price, only value."

Bel Kaufman

Name

✉

☎

Name

✉

☎

Name

✉

☎

Name

✉

☎

Name

✉

☎

Name

✉

☎

STEPFAMILY ASSOCIATION
071-372 0844/0846
(2-5pm & 7-10pm weekdays)
72 Willesden Lane, London NW6 7TA

The Association offers telephone support, advice and information for all members of stepfamilies and encouragement to develop self-help groups. Regular publications are available.

ST JOHN'S AMBULANCE
071-235 5231
1 Grosvenor Crescent, London SW1X 7EF

Divisions provide First Aid courses for adults and children. Crutches and wheelchair hire are available. See your local directory for nearest centre.

STROKE ASSOCIATION
071-490 7999
CHSA House, Whitecross Street, London EC1Y 8JJ

Works for the prevention of stroke disease, and rehabilitation of stroke sufferers. The Association also publishes books and leaflets.

TERRENCE HIGGINS TRUST
071-242 1010 (helpline: 3pm-10pm)
071-405 2381 (legal line: Weds 7pm-10pm)
52-54 Gray's Inn Road, London WC1X 8JU

The Trust offers a telephone helpline, providing one-to-one support (including a buddying service) and counselling to people with AIDS/HIV, their friends and families. It runs self-help groups, and provides information and advice on all aspects of AIDS/HIV, including social, legal, psychological and political effects. Publications are available.

VICTIMS' HELP LINE
071-729 1252 (24 hour)
St. Leonard's, Nuttall Street, London N1 5LZ

Offering a 24-hour confidential helpline for victims of any crime and their families and providing telephone counselling, information and referral service.

WAR (WOMEN AGAINST RAPE)
071-837 7509
71 Tonbridge Street, London WC1H 9DZ

Offering support and advice to women surviving rape and other violence. It campaigns to end rape in all its forms, including rape in marriage. Publications are available.

WOMEN'S AID FEDERATION
0272-633542
PO Box 391, Bristol BS99 7WS

Offering temporary refuge for women and their children who are threatened by mental, emotional, or physical violence, harassment, or sexual abuse. The national office provides a helpline for advice and information. There is a network of 200 local groups in the UK. Publications are available.

WOMEN'S NATIONWIDE CANCER CONTROL CAMPAIGN
071-729 2229
Suna House, 128-130 Curtain Rd, London EC2A 3AR

WNCCC aims to help women overcome their fears about cancer, providing information about early detection and prevention. Send SAE for full range of educational literature. Confidential helpline Mon-Fri 9.30-4.30pm. Information tapes available 24 hours.

EVERYDAY THOUGHTS
for everyday living

"Blessed be childhood, which brings
down something of heaven into the
midst of our rough earthliness."

Henri Frédéric Amiel

"An agreeable companion on a journey
is as good as a carriage."

Publilius Syrus

"What value has compassion that does
not take its object in its arms?"

Saint-Exupéry

"Worse than idle is compassion
If it ends in tears and sighs."

William Wordsworth

"Content makes poor men rich;
discontent makes rich men poor."

Benjamin Franklin

Addresses • Addresses • Addresses • Addresses • Addresses • Addresses • Addresses • Addresses

Name

✉

☎

Name

✉

☎

Name

✉

☎

Name

✉

☎

Name

✉

☎

Name

✉

☎

IN THE KITCHEN ~ WEIGHTS, MEASURES & TEMPERATURES

COOKING (DIAL MARKINGS)

Gasmark	1/4	1	2	3	4
Fahrenheit	250	275	300	325	350
Celsius	120	140	150	160	180

Gasmark	5	6	7	8	9
Fahrenheit	375	400	425	450	475
Celsius	190	200	220	230	240

OVEN TEMPERATURES

Gasmark	Description
1/4	Very Slow
1/2	Very Slow
1	Slow
2	Slow
3	Moderate
4	Moderate
5	Moderately Hot
6	Moderately Hot
7	Hot
8	Hot
9	Very Hot

Conversions given are approximate.
Never mix metric and imperial measures in one recipe - stick to one system or the other.

TEMPERATURE CONVERSION CHART

°F	°C
212B	100B
122	50
113	45
104	40
95	35
86	30
77	25
68	20
59	15
50	10
41	5
32	0
23	-5
14	-10
5	-15
-4	-20

DRY WEIGHT

Approximate gram conversion to nearest round figure	Recommended gram conversion to nearest 25g	Imperial ounce (oz)
28	25	1
57	50	2
85	75	3
113	100-125	4 (1/4lb)
142	150	5
170	175	6
198	200	7
227	225	8 (1/2lb)
255	250	9
284	275	10
311	300	11
340	350	12 (3/4lb)
368	375	13
396	400	14
425	425	15
453	450	16 (1lb)

LIQUID MEASURES

Approx. mililitre conversion to nearest round figure	Recommended mililitre equivalent	Imperial pint	Imperial fluid ounce (oz)
568	575-600	1	20
284	300	1/2	10
142	150	1/4	5

24

EVERYDAY THOUGHTS
for everyday living

"It is always darkest just before the day dawneth."

Thomas Fuller

"To die completely, a person must not only forget but be forgotten, and he who is not forgotten is not dead."

Samuel Butler

"Oh, what a tangled web we weave
When first we practise to deceive."

Walter Scott: Marmion

"Despair exaggerates not only our misery but also our weakness."

Luc de Vauvenargues

"Despair of nothing.
[Nil desperandum]."

Latin Proverb

𝔇

Name
✉

☎

Name
✉

☎

Name
✉

☎

Name
✉

☎

Name
✉

☎

Name
✉

☎

FOOD & HEALTH

CALORIE EXPENDITURE

Below are given the approximate energy costs of some activities for a 70 kg adult:

Activity	Calories used per 15 min	Activity	Calories used per 15 min
Sitting	20	Energetic dancing	85
Sweeping	30	Judo, karate, tai'chi	90
Sitting, writing	35	Skating, roller skating	90
Sailing	40	Playing cricket - batting	100
Driving a car	48	Playing tennis	120
Table tennis	50	Jogging	120
Yoga	50	Digging	130
Walking slowly	55		
Ironing	60		
Cycling slowly	65		
Surfing/wind surfing	65		
Polishing floor	68		
Water skiing	70		
Badminton	70	Playing football	140
		Shovelling earth	160
		Cycling fast	168
		Skiing downhill	175
		Climbing with a pack	200
		Running	200
Golf	75	Squash	230
Walking fast	80	Swimming fast	255
Ballet	80	Skiing cross-country	280

EVERYDAY THOUGHTS
for everyday living

"Difficulties strengthen the mind, as labour does the body."

Seneca

"The best way out of a difficulty is through it."

Author Unidentified

"What we hope to do with ease, we must first learn to do with diligence."

Samuel Johnson

"Our duty is to be useful, not according to our desires, but according to our powers."

Henri Frédérick Amiel

"The path of duty lies in the thing that is nearby, but men seek it in things far off."

Chinese Proverb

𝕯

Name
✉

☎
Name
✉

☎
Name
✉

☎
Name
✉

☎
Name
✉

☎
Name
✉

☎

FOOD & HEALTH ~ CALORIE COUNTING

Calories per ounce (25g) unless otherwise stated:

Anchovies	40
Apples	10
Apricots	
Canned in syrup	30
Dried	50
Fresh, with stone	5
Artichokes (boiled)	5
Asparagus	5
Aubergines	5
Sliced & fried (1oz raw)	60
Avocado Pears (flesh only)	65
Bacon	
Back raw	120
Streaky raw	115
Bananas (flesh only)	20
Bass (steamed fillet)	35
Bean Sprouts (raw)	10
Beans	
Baked beans	20
Broad (boiled)	15
Butter (boiled)	25
French (boiled)	neg
Haricot (boiled)	30
Kidney (canned)	25
Runner (boiled)	5
Soya (raw, dried)	115
Beef	
Brisket (boiled)	90
Minced beef (raw)	75
Minced beef (1oz raw, well fried & drained of fat)	45
Rump steak (fried, lean)	55
Rump steak (grilled, lean)	50
Sirloin (roast, lean & fat)	50
Stewing steak (raw)	50
Topside (roast, lean & fat)	60
Beetroot (boiled)	15
Blackberries (fresh)	10
Blackcurrants (fresh)	10
Black Pudding (raw)	105
Bran	60
Bread	
Brown/Wheatmeal/Hovis/White	65
Malt	70
Wholemeal	60
Bap (50g)	120
Croissant (50g)	270
Crusty roll	145
French Bread (50g)	130
Granary	70
Hot cross bun (50g)	180
Pitta bread (45g)	125
Rye bread	70
Tea cake (50g)	155
Broccoli (boiled)	5
Brussels Sprouts (boiled)	5
Butter	210
Cabbage (boiled)	5
Carrots (boiled)	5
Cauliflower (boiled)	5
Caviar	75
Celery	neg
Cheese	
Austrian Smoked	80
Babybel	95
Blue Stilton	130
Boursin	115
Brie	90
Cairphilly	120
Camembert	90
Cheddar	120
Cheshire	110
Cottage Cheese	25
Cream Cheese	125
Curd Cheese	40
Danish Blue	105
Danish Mozzarella	100
Double Gloucester	105
Edam	90
Emmenthal	115
Gorgonzola	110
Gouda (not matured)	95
Gruyere	130
Lancashire	110
Leicester	105
Norwegian Blue	100
Parmesan	115
Processed	90
Rambol (with walnuts)	115
Roquefort	90
Sage Derby	110
Wensleydale	115
White Stilton	95
Cherries	
Fresh with stones	10
Glace	60
Chicken	
On bone, raw	25
Meat only, raw	40
Meat & skin, roast	60
Chinese Leaves	neg
Chives	10
Chocolate	
Milk/Plain	150
Cooking	155
Cod	
On bone, raw	15
Fillet, raw	20
Fried in batter	55
Steamed fillet	25
Coffee (instant)	30
Corned Beef	60
Corn o/t Cob (boiled, kernels only)	35
Courgettes	5
Cream	
Clotted	165
Double	125
Single	60
Soured	55
Whipping	95
Cucumber	5
Currants	70
Dates (per date)	15
Duck	
Roast, meat only	55
Roast, meat, fat & skin	95

EVERYDAY THOUGHTS
for everyday living

"Early rising not only gives us more life in the same number of years, but adds, likewise, to their number."

Charles Cotton

"Education is what survives when what has been learnt has been forgotten."

B F Skinner

"Education is an ornament in prosperity and a refuge in adversity."

Aristotle

"Correction does much, but encouragement does more."

Johann Wolfgang von Goethe

"Love your enemies, bless them that curse you, do good to them that hate you, and pray for them which despitefully use you, and persecute you."

Matthew 5:44

𝔈

Name

✉

☎

Name

✉

☎

Name

✉

☎

Name

✉

☎

Name

✉

☎

Name

✉

☎

Name

✉

☎

FOOD & HEALTH ~ CALORIE COUNTING

Eggs

Graded Eggs	Raw	Fried
1	95	145
2	90	140
3	80	130
4	75	120
5	70	110
6	60	100
Yolk of size 3 egg		60
White of size 3 egg		15

Gherkins	5
Gooseberries (fresh, dessert)	10
Grapefruit	
Canned in syrup	15
Flesh only/With skin	5
Juice	10
Grapes	15
Haddock	
On bone, raw	15
Fillet, raw	20
On bone, smoked	20
Smoked fillet	30
Fried fillet in breadcrumbs	50
Hake	
On bone, raw	10
Fillet, raw	20
Fillet, steamed	30
Fillet, fried	60
Halibut	
On bone, steamed	30
Fillet, steamed	35
Ham	
Lean, boiled	60
Fatty, boiled	120
Herring	
On bone, grilled	40
Fillet, grilled	55
Honey	80
Ice-cream	45
Jam	75
Kidney (raw)	25
Kippers (baked or grilled fillet)	60
Lamb	
Roast breast, boned,	115
Roast breast, boned, lean only	75
Roast leg, boned,	75
Roast leg, boned, lean only	55
Roast shoulder, lean & fat	90
Roast shoulder, lean only	55
Leeks (raw)	10
Lemon Sole	
On bone (grilled or steamed)	20
Fillet (grilled or steamed)	25
Lentils (boiled)	30
Lettuce (raw)	5
Liver	
Chicken's, fried	55
Lamb's, fried	65
Ox, stewed	55
Pig's, stewed	55
Liver sausage	90
Lobster	
With shell, boiled	10
Meat only, boiled	35
Macaroni (boiled)	35
Mackerel	
On bone, fried	40
Fillet, fried	55
Smoked	70
Mandarins	
Canned	15
Fresh, with skin	5
Margarine	205
Marmalade	75
Marzipan	125
Mayonnaise	205
Melon (with skin)	5
Milk	
Gold Top	430
Red Top	370
Longlife/UHT	370
Low-fat powdered	200
Pasteurised/Silver Top	370
Skimmed	200
Sterilized	370
Evaporated	45
Condensed (sweetened)	90
Muesli	105
Mushrooms (raw)	5
Mussels	
Boiled, with shells	5
Boiled, without shells	25
Nectarines	15
Noodles (cooked)	35
Nuts (mixed, roasted, salted)	175
Olive Oil	255
Olives (with stones, in brine)	25
Onions	
Raw	5
Fried	100
Rings fried in batter	145
Oranges	
Flesh only	10
With skin	5
Juice	10
Parsnips (raw or boiled)	15
Peaches	
Fresh, with stones	10
Canned in syrup	25
Peanuts	
Shelled or roasted, salted	160
Peanut butter	175
Pears	
Fresh	10
Canned in syrup	20
Peas	
Fresh, raw	20
Fresh, boiled	15
Canned, garden	15

Canned, processed	25
Chick, raw	90
Perch	
White	35
Yellow	25
Pheasant	
Roast, on bone	40
Roast, meat only	60
Pilchards (canned in tomato sauce)	35

EVERYDAY THOUGHTS
for everyday living

"Let age, not envy, draw wrinkles on thy cheeks."

Sir Thomas Browne

"The quality of a person's life is in direct proportion to their commitment to excellence, regardless of their chosen field of endeavour."

Vince Lombardi

"He that is good for making excuses is seldom good for anything else."

Benjamin Franklin

"Experience is not what happens to you; it is what you do with what happens to you."

Aldous Huxley

"To most men, experience is like the stern lights of a ship, which illumine only the track it has passed."

S T Coleridge

Addresses • Addresses • Addresses • Addresses • Addresses • Addresses • Addresses • Addresses

E

Name

✉

☎

Name

✉

☎

Name

✉

☎

Name

✉

☎

Name

✉

☎

Name

✉

☎

Pineapples		Canned	45	Fudge	110
Fresh	15	Smoked	40	Peppermints	110
Canned in syrup	20	Sardines		Toffee	120
Plaice (fillet)		Canned in oil, drained	60	Syrup	
Raw or steamed	25	Canned in tomato sauce	50	Golden	85
Fried in batter	80	Sausages		Maple	70
Fried in crumbs	65	Pork, lightly fried or grilled	165	Tangerines	
Plums		Pork, well fried or grilled	115	Flesh only	10
Fresh dessert, with stones	10	Pork, chipolata:		With skin	5
Cooking, with stones	5	lightly fried or grilled	165	Tapioca (dry)	100
Pork		well fried or grilled	115	Tea	neg
Roast, lean & fat	80	Beef, fried or grilled	120	Tomatoes	
Roast, lean meat only	50	Beef, chipolata fried or grilled	120	Canned	5
Cracking	190	Scampi (fried in breadcrumbs)	90	Fried, halved	20
Scratchings	185	Semolina (raw)	100	Fried, sliced	30
Prawns		Shrimps		Ketchup	30
With shells	10	With shells	10	Puree	20
Without shells	30	Without shells	35	Raw	5
		Canned	25	Tongue (Ox, boiled)	85
		Skate (fillet fried in batter)	55	Treacle (Black)	85
		Sole		Tripe (Stewed)	30
		Fillet, raw	25	Trout	
		Fillet, fried	60	Fillet, smoked	35
		Fillet, steamed	25	On bone, steamed	25
		On bone, steamed	20	Tuna	
		Spaghetti		Canned in oil	80
		Raw	105	Drained of oil	60
Prunes		Boiled	35	Turkey	
Dried	45	Canned in tomato sauce	15	Meat only, roast	40
Stewed (no sugar)	25	Spinach (boiled)	10	Meat & skin, roast	50
Rabbit		Spring Onions	10	Turnips (raw)	5
On bone, stewed	25	Strawberries		Veal	
Meat only, stewed	50	Fresh	5	Escalope, fried (egg/b'crumbs)	60
Radishes	5	Tinned, drained	25	Fillet, raw	30
Raspberries		Sturgeon (on bone, raw)	25	Fillet, roast	65
Fresh	5	Sugar	110	Venison (roast, meat)	55
Tinned, drained	25	Sultanas (dried)	70	Watermelon	5
Redcurrants (fresh)	5	Sunflower Seed Oil	255	Whitebait (fried)	150
Rhubarb	neg	Swedes	5	Whiting	
Rice		Sweetcorn		On bone, fried	50
Raw	100	Canned	20	Fillet, fried	55
Boiled	35	Fresh boiled, kernels	35	On bone, steamed	20
Salmon		Frozen	25	Fillet, steamed	25
Raw, on bone	50	Sweets		Yorkshire Pudding (cooked)	60
Steamed, on bone	45	Boiled sweets	95		
Steamed, fillet	55	Filled chocolates	130	'neg' signifies negligible calorie content	

EVERYDAY THOUGHTS
for everyday living

"If your life is free of failures, you're not taking enough risks."

Author Unidentified

"There is no failure except in no longer trying."

Elbert Hubbard

"Only the person who has faith in himself is able to be faithful to others."

Erich Fromm

"The greatest of faults is to be conscious of none."

Thomas Carlyle

"Present fears are less than horrible imaginings."

Shakespeare: Macbeth

𝔉

Name

✉

☎

Name

✉

☎

Name

✉

☎

Name

✉

☎

Name

✉

☎

Name

✉

☎

IN THE KITCHEN ~ VEGETABLES

Cooking Times & Methods of Some Vegetables

Vegetable	Steam	Boil	Bake (Whole)	Braise	Stir Fry
Asparagus		10-15 mins			
Beetroot		40-60 mins			
Broad Beans		10-15 mins			
Broccoli	4-8 mins				yes
Brussels Sprouts	6-10 mins		25-30 mins		yes
Cabbage	4-6 mins				yes
Carrots	20 mins	10-15 mins	45-60 mins	15-20 mins	yes
Cauliflower	4-8 mins				
Celery	12-15 mins	8-10 mins		10-12 mins	yes
Chicory					yes
Chinese Leaves	4 mins				yes
Courgettes	4-8 mins				yes
Cucumbers	5-10 mins				
Endive				10-12 mins	
Fennel	12-15 mins	10-12 mins		15-20 mins	yes
French Beans	4-8 mins				yes
Globe Artichokes		30-40 mins			
Jerusalem Artichokes		15-20 mins			
Leeks	15-20 mins	10-15 mins		8-10 mins	
Mangetout Peas	6-8 mins				yes
Marrow	10-12 mins		45-60 mins		yes
Mushrooms					yes
Okra		15-20 mins			
Onions			45-60 mins		
Parsnips		15-20 mins	45-60 mins	15-20 mins	
Peas		8-12 mins			yes
Peppers					yes
Potatoes	25-30 mins	20 mins	1-1½ hours	15-20 mins	
Radish/Daikon					yes
Red Cabbage				45-60 mins	
Swedes	25-30 mins	20 mins		15-20 mins	yes
Sweet Potato	25-30 mins	20 mins	1-1½ hours		
Sweetcorn		8-15 mins			yes
Turnips	25-30 mins	10-15 mins		15-20 mins	yes

These are suggestions only and will give very lightly cooked vegetables. Increase the cooking time for softer vegetables. The freshness of the vegetables may also affect the cooking time.

EVERYDAY THOUGHTS
for everyday living

"The only thing we have to fear is fear itself."

F. D. Roosevelt

"Forgiveness is the answer to the child's dream of a miracle by which what is broken is made whole again, what is soiled is again made clean."

Dag Hammarskjold

"I keep my friends as misers do their treasure, because, of all the things granted us by wisdom, none is greater or better than friendship."

Pietro Aretino

"A true friend is the greatest of all blessings."

La Rochefoucauld

"I like the dreams of the future better than the history of the past."

Thomas Jefferson

𝔉

Name

✉

☎

Name

✉

☎

Name

✉

☎

Name

✉

☎

Name

✉

☎

Name

✉

☎

IN THE KITCHEN ~ HERBS & SPICES

HERBS

Herbs play an essential role in any kitchen, adding flavour and distinction to many dishes. All are available fresh or dried but remember that fresh herbs have a milder flavour and use roughly 15ml (1 tablespoon) of fresh herbs to 5ml (1 teaspoon) of dried.

Basil (Ocimum basilicum)
Two types of basil are grown; sweet and bush. The one most commonly found is sweet basil, which has largish, shiny, green leaves and a strong but sweet flavour. It is one of the best herbs to add to tomatoes, eggs, mushrooms and pasta dishes, forms part of a classic bouquet garni, and is an essential part of pesto sauce. Basil does not dry very successfully.

Bay Leaves (Laurus nobilis)
Sweet bay or bay laurel is a Mediterranean tree. The leaves are shiny, smooth and dark with a strong aromatic scent. It is often added to stocks when poaching fish, or to marinades, casseroles, soups and stews. It can also be used to flavour milk puddings.

Chervil (Anthriscus cerefolium)
Chervil is a member of the parsley family and is very popular with French chefs. It has a delicate fern-like leaf, offering a delicate taste with a hint of anise. It is especially good in soups, egg and cheese dishes, or added for flavour to green salad. It can also be used as a garnishing leaf.

Chives (Allium schoenoprasum)
A member of the onion family, chives have a mild onion flavour and long, spiky, green leaves. Raw chives are frequently used in salads, but can be added to omelettes, cheese dishes, and, mixed with soured cream, used as a topping for baked potatoes.

Coriander (Coriandrum sativum)
Coriander has flat feathery leaves and is often confused with flat parsley. It has a distinctive spicy flavour and is popular in Southern European, Indian and South East Asian cooking. The leaves are chopped and added to curries, stews, soups and marinades. It is also known as Chinese or Japanese parsley, and is used in the same way as parsley.

Dill (Anethum graveolens)
A delicate, feathery herb with an aromatic, sharp but sweet flavour. One of the most popular herbs in Scandinavia, it is especially good with fish if added to the marinade, cooking liquid or accompanying sauces. It can also be added to vegetables, cream or cottage cheese.

Lemon Balm (Melissa officinalis)
The crushed leaves of this plant, as the name would suggest, give off a wonderful lemony scent, making them ideal for use in salads.

Marjoram (Origanum majorana)
Sweet marjoram, a plant native to the Mediterranean, has small, furry leaves and a flavour similar to oregano but sweeter and milder. It can be added to most savoury dishes and is good with marrow, potatoes and rice. It is very fragrant and can be dried successfully.

EVERYDAY THOUGHTS
for everyday living

"Generosity gives assitance rather
than advice."

Vauvenargues

"Genius is I per cent inspiration and
99 per cent perspiration."

Thomas A Edison

"Nothing is so strong as gentleness,
and nothing is so gentle as real
strength."

Ralph W Sockman

"The great mind knows the power
of gentleness,
Only tries force because
persuasion fails."

Robert Browning

"Grace is the absence of everything
that indicates pain or difficulty,
hesitation or incongruity."

William Hazlitt

Name

✉

☎

Name

✉

☎

Name

✉

☎

Name

✉

☎

Name

✉

☎

Name

✉

☎

IN THE KITCHEN ~ HERBS & SPICES

Mint (Menta spp.)

There are many species of this popular herb, from spearmint to the fresh-tasting peppermint used for tisanes. It is probably the best known herb in Britain and most commonly used with lamb and new potatoes. It can also be added to other young vegetables or chopped with minced beef, or mixed with yogurt for a dip. It also combines well with fruit.

Oregano (Origanum vulgare)

Oregano is wild marjoram, and, as it has the best flavour when grown in strong sun, is popular in Mediterranean cuisines - especially those of Italy and Greece. The flavour is similar to marjoram but stronger and the leaves are larger and darker. It enhances many meat dishes and it is often added to salads, pizza and tomato based dishes. Oregano can be dried successfully, keeping all its aroma.

Parsley (Petroselinum crispum)

There are two types of parsley: curled and flat. Flat (or French) parsley is generally grown in Europe and is considered to have a finer taste than curled parsley, but both are strong in Vitamin C and iron. Parsley is an essential part of a bouquet garni. It enlivens most savoury dishes and is often simply used as a garnish, either chopped or as sprigs. The chopped leaves can be added to salads, soups, sauces and cooked vegetables. It is said that if chewed after eating garlic it will remove the smell.

Rosemary (Rosmarinus officinalis)

A pungent, fragrant shrub with small, narrow leaves, set densely on the branches. It is often used with lamb but can be used with other meats and in vegetable dishes such as ratatouille or added to marinades.

Sage (Salvia officinalis)

Sage comes in many varieties and is a strongly flavoured herb with narrow, pale grey-green leaves with a rough texture. It has traditionally been used with pork, liver, and in stuffing, but can be used with any richly flavoured meat, and in cheese and tomato dishes. It dries well but can become musty if kept too long.

Savory (Satureja)

There are two varieties of savory: Winter savory (Satureja montana), and Summer savory (Satureja hortensis). The German name for winter savory means "bean-herb", indicating its traditional use, while summer savory is similar and even more aromatic.

Tarragon (Artemisia dracunculus)

There are two varieties of this herb: French and Russian. The French variety is harder to grow but is far more aromatic than the Russian. It has a distinctive flavour and shiny narrow leaves. It is widely used in vinegars, soups, stuffings, sauces, and salad dressings, and is also good with roast meat, poultry dishes and fish.

Thyme (Thymus vulgaris)

This popular herb contains an essential oil, thymol, which helps to digest fatty foods. Its small, dark-green bushy leaves have a very strong flavour. It is another herb which should be used in a bouquet garni, and it can be used to flavour meat, fish, soups, stews and vegetables.

EVERYDAY THOUGHTS
for everyday living

"Gratitude is the heart's memory."

French Proverb

"No metaphysician ever felt the
deficiency of language so much as the
grateful."

C C Colton

"A grateful mind, by owing owes not,
but still pays, at once
Indebted and discharged."

Milton: Paradise Lost

"Gratefulness is the poor man's
payment."

English Proverb

"The only cure for grief is action."

G H Lewes

"Nothing speaks our grief so well
As to speak nothing."

Richard Crashaw

𝕲

Name

✉

☎

Name

✉

☎

Name

✉

☎

Name

✉

☎

Name

✉

☎

Name

✉

☎

IN THE KITCHEN ~ HERBS & SPICES

Aniseed (Pimpinella asinum)
Aniseed has a strong liquorice flavour and is popular in Mexico and all over the Mediterranean.

Capers (Capparis spinosa)
The buds of a small Mediterranean bush, these are usually sold pickled in vinegar and should not be allowed to dry out. While they are used mostly in sauces and salads, they are also popular as a pizza topping, adding an authentic Mediterranean flavour.

Caraway (Carum carvi)
Caraway is in appearance similar to cumin seed and because of this is often confused with it. The taste, however, is very different.

Cardamom (Elettaria cardamomum)
Cardamom is a relative of the ginger family, available both whole green, black or white or ground. The most common is the grey-green pod which contains minute, dark brown seeds with an unmistakable bitter-sweet flavour with a hint of lemon and eucalyptus. It is used extensively in sweet and savoury Indian cookery as well as in Europe and the Middle East for cakes, biscuits and pickles and to flavour drinks.

Chili (Capsicum frutescens)
Ripe chili peppers dry and keep well and are most commonly used in chili powder, a very hot spice, whose blend may vary due to the numerous varieties of chilies to be found. Cayenne is a very hot, pungent red chili sold ready ground. Milder chili powders can be found or you can use chili seasoning which is a blend of ground dried chilis with other spices. It is used (sparingly) in meat, fish, poultry and egg dishes as well as soups, sauces and pickles.

Cinnamon (Cinnamomum zeylanicum)
The distinctive sticks of dried bark are harvested from the young shoots of a large, tropical evergreen. While it is best purchased as sticks and used whole or ground, is also available as a powder and has a sweet pungent flavour. Cinnamon is usually added to savoury dishes in the East and to sweet dishes in the West, and is used in apple desserts, cakes and mulled drinks.

Cloves (Eugenia caryophyllata)
Cloves are the unopened flower buds of the tropical evergreen clove tree. They become rich brown in colour when dried and resemble small nails in shape. Cloves have a penetrating taste and are available whole or ground: if used whole then they are best removed before a dish is eaten. They are used mainly to flavour fruit dishes, mulled wine, mincemeat, bread sauce and curries.

Coriander (Coriandrum sativum)
Coriander is a member of the parsley family. The aromatic brown seeds have a sweet orangey flavour. Sold whole or ground, they are quite mild so can be used more freely than most spices and are used widely in Arab and Eastern cookery; in curries, casseroles, soups, dishes such as couscous and hummus and with vegetables and chutneys.

EVERYDAY THOUGHTS
for everyday living

"We first make our habits, and
then our habits make us."
Author Unidentified

"Success is getting what you
want. Happiness is liking what
you get."
Author Unidentified

"Happiness makes up in height
for what it lacks in length."
Robert Frost

"We have no more right to consure
happiness without producing it than
to consume wealth without
producing it."
George Bernard Shaw

"When I was at home, I was in a
better place."
Shakespeare: As You Like It

Name

✉

☎

Name

✉

☎

Name

✉

☎

Name

✉

☎

Name

✉

☎

Name

✉

☎

IN THE KITCHEN ~ HERBS & SPICES

Cumin (Cuminum cyminum)
Cumin is a member of the parsley family and is available both as seeds or in powdered form. It has a sharp, spicy, slightly bitter taste and should be used in moderation. It is often combined with coriander as a basic curry mixture, but is also used for flavouring Middle Eastern fish recipes, casseroles and couscous. It can be added to pickles, chutneys, soups and rice dishes.

Ginger (Zingiber officinale)
Ginger is a distinctive knobbly root with a hot sweetish taste sold in several forms. Fresh root ginger, essential for many Eastern recipes, releases its true flavour on cooking. It is peeled and then sliced or grated for use in curries, Chinese cooking or marinades for meat, fish and poultry. Dried ginger is the dried ground root and is best used in preserves, cakes, biscuits and puddings. Stem ginger is available preserved in syrup or crystallized and is a sweetmeat either eaten whole, with carel, or used in breads, cakes, confectionery and desserts.

Juniper (Juniperus communis)
Juniper berries have a pungent, slightly resinous flavour. They go well with cabbage and add a light touch to oily or heavy dishes.

Mace (Myristica fragrans)
Mace is the dried outer membrane of nutmeg. It is sold both as blades or ground, although ground mace quickly loses its flavour. It is used in mulled wines and punches, meat pies, loaves, stews, savoury white sauces and in milk puddings.

Nutmeg (Myristica fragrans)
Nutmeg has a brown uneven outer surface with a pale interior, is milder than mace although slightly nuttier and is available whole or ground, but as it loses its flavour quickly, is best grated as required. It can be sprinkled on vegetables and is used in soups, sauces, meat terrines, pates, and puddings.

Paprika (Capsicum annum)
A finely ground red powder made from the fruits of several chili plants, popular in Hungary and Spain. The flesh only is used for mild sweet paprikas whilst the seeds are included in more pungent paprikas. Use to add colour to egg and cheese dishes, in salads, with fish and shellfish, chicken and classically in Hungarian Goulash.

Saffron (Crocus sativus)
Saffron is the dried stigmas of the saffron crocus flower. It is very expensive, as it is individually handpicked and imparts a slightly bitter honey-like flavour and a yellow colour. It is safer to buy the threads as the powder is easy to adulterate. It is added to rice dishes, Spanish Paella, Bouillabaisse and to Cornish Saffron cake.

Turmeric (Circuma longa)
Turmeric is the dried root of a plant from the ginger family, usually sold ground, although sometimes sold fresh. It has a strong woody aroma and a slightly bitter flavour and is used to colour rice, pickles, cakes and in curries and dhals. It is sometimes used as a cheap substitute for saffron to colour dishes, but the flavour is not the same.

Vanilla (Vanilla planifolia)
Vanilla is the fruit of an orchid plant found in Mexico. It has traditionally been used to flavour chocolate, and is good in many sweet dishes, though it is expensive to buy.

EVERYDAY THOUGHTS
for everyday living

"We should not let our fears hold us
back from pursuing our hopes."

John F Kennedy

"The hope set before us . . . is like an
anchor for our lives, an anchor safe
and sure."

Hebrews 6.19

"When there is room in the heart
there is room in the house."

Danish Proverb

"Hospitality is to be shown even
towards an enemy. The tree doth
not withdraw its shade, even
from the woodcutter."

The Hitopadesa

"Better is it to be of a humble
spirit with the lowly than to
divide the spoil with the proud."

Proverbs 16:19

Addresses • Addresses • Addresses • Addresses • Addresses • Addresses • Addresses • Addresses

H

Name
✉

☎

Name
✉

☎

Name
✉

☎

Name
✉

☎

Name
✉

☎

Name
✉

☎

IN THE KITCHEN ~ INTERNATIONAL RECIPES

FROM TURKEY

CACIK
Ingredients

1 cucumber

2-3 cloves garlic

3/4 pint yogurt

3 tbsp chopped mint

Salt, white pepper

Method

Peel & dice cucumber, then sprinkle with salt and leave in colander for half an hour. Crush garlic with a little salt, add to yogurt and mix well. Add salt, pepper and mint, drain cucumber and stir in. Garnish with mint.

IMAM BAYILDI
Ingredients

3 large onions

3 large aubergines (with leaf bases cut off)

Olive oil

1 clove garlic

12 oz tomatoes

1 tbsp chopped parsley

1/2 tsp cinnamon

1 heaped tbsp finely chopped pine kernels (optional)

1 tsp castor sugar

Salt, black pepper

Method

Wipe the aubergines and put in large saucepan. Add boiling water and cover. Cook for 10 mins, drain, then plunge into cold water. Leave for 5 mins, cut in half lengthways, scoop out most of flesh, leaving half-inch thick shells. Arrange shells in buttered overproof dish and sprinkle with salt and pepper. Pour 4 tbsp olive oil into each shell and cook, uncovered, in pre-heated oven (350°F or equivalent) for 30 mins. While aubergines are cooking, peel and finely chop onions, skin and chop tomatoes and crush garlic. Heat 2 tbsp of oil in a frying pan, add onions and garlic and fry gently for 5 mins, then add tomatoes, cinnamon, sugar and parsley; season to taste. Simmer until liquid has reduced by half (about 20 mins). Chop aubergine flesh and add to frying pan with pine kernels and cook for 10 mins. Remove aubergine shells from oven, stuff with tomato mixture and serve hot or cold.

TURKISH YOGURT
Ingredients

2 cartons natural yogurt

1 tbsp lemon juice

1 tsp castor sugar

1 tsp lemon rind

2 oz seedless raisins

1 tbsp desiccated coconut

Method

Mix all ingredients together, put in covered dish and chill. Leave to stand for at least one hour before serving to allow flavour to develop.

EVERYDAY THOUGHTS
for everyday living

"Man's mind once stretched by a new
idea, never regains its original
dimension."

Oliver Wendell Holmes

"Idleness, like kisses, to be sweet
must be stolen."

Jerome K Jerome

"There is always hope in a man who
actually and earnestly works.
In idleness alone is there perpetual
despair."

Thomas Carlyle

"The man with imagination is
never alone."

Author Unidentified

"By asking for the impossible we
obtain the best possible."

Italian Proverb

𝕵

Name

✉

☎

Name

✉

☎

Name

✉

☎

Name

✉

☎

Name

✉

☎

Name

✉

☎

IN THE KITCHEN ~ INTERNATIONAL RECIPES

FROM GREECE

TARAMASALATA
Ingredients

8 oz smoked cod roe (fresh or tinned)　Juice of 1 large lemon
6-8 tbsp olive oil　Black pepper

Method

Place roe in a mixing bowl. Add oil and lemon juice alternately, a little at a time, and beat vigorously after each addition until the mixture is a creamy paté. Season to taste with freshly ground black pepper and pack into a dish. Cover and chill lightly. Serve with hot crisp toast, unsalted butter, black olives and lemon wedges.

DOLMADES
Ingredients

12 fresh vine/cabbage leaves or a 7 oz tin of vine leaves

1 lb lean lamb, minced　1 dsp chopped fresh mint or parsley
1 onion　1 tsp powdered rosemary
4 oz long grain rice　Salt, black pepper
3 oz butter　Juice of half a lemon
1 ½ pints of white stock　5 fl oz yogurt

Method

Peel onion and chop finely. Melt 1 oz butter and fry onion and rice until lightly coloured. Add enough stock to cover rice and cook over low heat until tender, stirring frequently. Leave to cool. Stir in minced lamb, herbs and salt and pepper. Blanch the fresh vine or cabbage leaves for a few minutes in boiling water, spread out and put a spoonful of lamb and rice filling on each; fold the leaves over to make small, neat parcels. Pack carefully in layers in casserole pan. Put a plate on top to keep the parcels under the liquid. Cover and simmer for one hour. Serve yogurt separately.

HISTORIAN'S PUDDING
Ingredients

2 oz self-raising flour　1 oz sugar
4 oz fresh breadcrumbs　2 chopped dried figs
4 oz suet　Grated rind of ½ lemon
8 oz raisins　2 eggs, beaten
1 tbsp allspice　2 tbsp sherry
1 tbsp milk

Method

Mix all dry ingredients together. Stir in eggs and sherry, then add milk to make a soft dough. Put in buttered pudding basin and cover with foil. Steam for 3-4 hours and serve hot with sherry sauce.

EVERYDAY THOUGHTS
for everyday living

"Nature knows no pause in her progress and developement, and attaches her curse on all inaction."

Johann Wolfgang von Goethe

"He's armed without that's innocent within."

Alexander Pope

"A man is not to aim at innocence any more than he is to aim at hair, but he is to keep it."

Ralph Waldo Emerson

"A moment's insight is sometimes worth a life's experience."

O. W. Holmes

"Instinct is intelligence incapable of selfconciousness."

John Sterling

Addresses • Addresses • Addresses • Addresses • Addresses • Addresses • Addresses • Addresses

𝕵

Name

✉

☎

Name

✉

☎

Name

✉

☎

Name

✉

☎

Name

✉

☎

Name

✉

☎

IN THE KITCHEN ~ INTERNATIONAL RECIPES

FROM AMERICA

TUNA WALDORF SALAD
Ingredients

2 7-oz tins of tuna
1 cup diced apples
$\frac{1}{2}$ cup chopped celery
Crumbled blue cheese

$\frac{1}{4}$ cup walnuts
$\frac{1}{2}$ cup mayonnaise
Lettuce

Method

Drain and flake the tuna. In a bowl combine all ingredients except lettuce and blue cheese. Mix well. Serve on lettuce leaves. Garnish with crumbled blue cheese.

SLOPPY JOES
Ingredients

1 lb minced beef
1 large onion
1 green pepper
2 tbsp American mustard
1 tsp brown sugar

2 tsp cloves
2 tsp white sugar
2 tsp vinegar
Tomato ketchup
10 bread rolls

Method

Chop the onion and the green pepper and fry the meat until it is brown. Then add the rest of the ingredients. Mix together and fry for about 10 minutes. 'Slop' onto hamburger style buns.

PUMPKIN PIE
Ingredients
For the Pastry:

6 oz plain flour
3 oz butter
Milk or water
Pinch of salt

4 oz soft brown sugar
1 tsp cinnamon
1 tsp mace
$\frac{1}{4}$ tsp ground nutmeg

For the Filling:

1 14-oz tin pumpkin (or fresh pumpkin)
$\frac{1}{4}$ pint milk
2 eggs, lightly beaten

1 $\frac{1}{2}$ tsp salt
$\frac{1}{4}$ pint single cream

Method

Preheat oven to 450°F. Prepare blind pastry shell but do not bake it. Combine all the filling ingredients, mixing well. Pour into the pie crust. Bake in oven for 15 mins, then lower temperature to 350°F and bake till firm - about another 50 mins. Serve warm or cold with grated cheese on top or with cream.

EVERYDAY THOUGHTS
for everyday living

"Though jealousy be produced by love, as ashes are by fire, yet jealousy extinguishes love as ashes smother the flame."

Margaret of Navarre

"It is not love that is blind, but jealousy."

Lawrence Durrell

"Jealousy: that dragon which slays love under the pretense of keeping it alive."

Havelock Ellis

"A wise man sings his joy in the closet of his heart."

Tibullus

"All who joy would win
Must share it, -
Happiness was born a Twin."

Byron: Don Juan

𝕵

Name

✉

☎

Name

✉

☎

Name

✉

☎

Name

✉

☎

Name

✉

☎

Name

✉

☎

IN THE KITCHEN ~ INTERNATIONAL RECIPES

FROM FRANCE

FRENCH ONION SOUP
Ingredients

2 oz butter or margarine
2 large onions
2 pints of stock

Sliced French bread
Grated Gruyère cheese
Seasoning

Method

Slice onion thinly and fry in butter, add the stock and simmer for about 30 minutes. Season with salt and pepper. Meanwhile, sprinkle cheese on bread slices and brown under a hot grill. Put bread in bottom of soup bowls and pour soup on top.

QUICHE LORRAINE
Ingredients

8 oz shortcrust pastry
I onion
4 rashers bacon
I small leek, chopped

$1/4$ pint milk
3 eggs
2 oz grated cheese
Seasoning

Method

Make pastry and with it line a deep 7-inch sandwich tin, or a flan ring or a I pint deep ovenproof plate. Chop the onion and bacon into small pieces and then fry in margarine until tender. Turn them into the pastry case. Beat eggs, stir in the milk, seasoning and most of the cheese, and add the chopped leek. Pour this mixture into the case, sprinkle rest of cheese on top. Bake the flan until it is just set and golden brown on top, 350°F or Gas Mark 5 for 35-40 minutes.

FRENCH CUSTARD ICE CREAM
Ingredients

2 large eggs
$1/2$ pint single cream

3 tbsp granulated sugar
2 tsp vanilla essence

Method

Set fridge to its coldest setting one hour before making ice cream. Place cream, eggs and sugar into a double saucepan with water simmering. Sitr continuously until the custard is thick enough to coat thinly the back of a spoon. Do not let it boil. Pour into a bowl, stir in the vanilla essence and cool. Pour when cold into ice cube tray and place in the freezer section of your fridge. Freeze until ice cream has frozen about $1/2$ inch round sides of tray (about I hour). Turn into chilled bowl and whisk until smooth. Return to washed and dried tray and freeze until firm (a further $1^{1}/_{2}$ to 2 hours).

EVERYDAY THOUGHTS
for everyday living

"He who binds to himself a joy
Does the winged life destroy;
But he who kisses the joy as it flies
Lives in eternity's sunrise."

William Blake

"Joy is for all men. It does not depend
on circumstance or condition: if it did,
it could only be for the few."

Horace Bushnell

"If you judge, investigate."
[Si judicas, cognosce.]

Seneca

"He hath a good judgement that
relieth not wholly on his own."

Thomas Fuller

"Extreme justice is often unjust.'"

Racine

Name	ℑ
✉	
☎	
Name	
✉	
☎	
Name	
✉	
☎	
Name	
✉	
☎	
Name	
✉	
☎	
Name	
✉	
☎	

Addresses • Addresses • Addresses • Addresses • Addresses • Addresses • Addresses • Addresses

IN THE KITCHEN ~ INTERNATIONAL RECIPES

FROM JAPAN

NABEMONO (COD SOUP)
Ingredients

2 fillets cod

3 leeks

Chinese leaves or spinach

12 mushrooms

2 packets bean cake (available from health food shops)

Soya sauce

Method

Cut cod into small pieces and cut bean cake into cubes. Wash vegetables and put water in large saucepan. When hot but not boiling, add fish and bean cake. Bring to boil and skim off froth. Add all the vegetables. Simmer for 10 minutes.

TAKIKOMI GOHAN (CHICKEN RICE)
Ingredients

4 cups pudding rice

3 tbsp Saki or white wine

Soya sauce

1 pinch salt

1 carrot

3 mushrooms

$1/4$ chicken

$1/2$ lb french beans

Method

Wash rice until the water is clear and leave to drain for 30 minutes. Slice carrot and mushrooms and cut chicken into very small pieces. Put about 4 $1/2$ cups of water in saucepan, add rice and all ingredients except the beans. Bring to boil on high heat then remove lid. Leave boiling hard for 2 minutes. When water is almost gone and air holes appear in rice, turn heat down very low. Meanwhile boil french beans very lightly in salted water. Chop up with butter and mix with rice before serving.

YAKITOR (CHICKEN)
Ingredients

4 chicken pieces

Soya sauce

Saki or white wine

Ground ginger

1 red chili

1 garlic clove

Method

Chop chili and garlic and wash chicken. Put all ingredients in dish and leave overnight, turning occasionally. Before the meal, grill the chicken.

This can be served with raw vegetables or salad, cucumber, tomatoes, chopped cabbage, grated carrots, lettuce etc.

EVERYDAY THOUGHTS
for everyday living

"You can accomplish by kindness
what you cannot do by force."

Publilius Syrus

"One who knows how to show and
to accept kindness will be a friend
better than any possession."

Sophocles

"I expect to pass through life but
once. If, therefore, there be any
kindness I can show, or any good
thing I can do for any fellow being,
let me do it now, for I shall not pass
this way again."

William Penn

"The smallest act of kindness is worth
more than the grandest intention."

Author Unidentified

Addresses • Addresses • Addresses • Addresses • Addresses • Addresses • Addresses

𝕶

Name
✉
☎

Name
✉
☎

Name
✉
☎

Name
✉
☎

Name
✉
☎

Name
✉
☎

IN THE KITCHEN ~ INTERNATIONAL RECIPES

FROM ITALY

SPAGHETTI BOLOGNESE
Ingredients

I onion	¹/₄ lb mushrooms
I ¹/₂ oz butter	I 5oz tin tomato purée
I dsp olive oil	2 tsp sugar
¹/₂ lb minced beef	¹/₂ tsp mixed herbs
¹/₂ pint water	³/₄ lb spaghetti
4 oz Cheddar cheese	Seasoning
I garlic clove	Bay leaf

Method

Chop onion and fry gently, add meat and fry for 4 minutes, stirring. Add chopped garlic and sliced mushrooms together with water, sugar, bay leaf, tomato purée, herbs and seasoning. Bring to boil and simmer for 30 minutes, stirring often. Boil spaghetti for 20 minutes in salted water. Drain and serve with sauce and finely grated cheese.

RISOTTO MILANESE
Ingredients

I small onion	³/₄ lb long grain rice
3 oz butter	3 oz cheese
I ¹/₂ pints chicken stock	Seasoning

Method

Fry chopped onion gently in 2 oz butter. Add rice and fry for I minute, stirring Gradually add hot stock. Simmer in covered pan for 25 minutes, stirring often. Add I oz butter and I oz cheese. Serve with grated cheese.

MILANESE SOUFFLE
Ingredients

2 lemons	¹/₂ oz gelatine
3 eggs, separated	5 tbsp water
4 oz sugar	Chopped nuts, whipped cream, glacé cherries & angelica
¹/₂ pint double cream	(for decoration)

Method

Dissolve gelatine in water, using bowl in saucepan of warm water. To another bowl in warm water add egg yolks, sugar, juice and grated rinds from lemons, whisking until thick and creamy. Remove from heat and whisk until the outside of the bowl is cold. Fold in lightly whipped cream, then add whisked egg whites and finally the gelatine. Pour mixture into souffle case and chill. Stand on large plate and decorate with chopped nuts, whipped cream, glacé cherries and angelica.

EVERYDAY THOUGHTS
for everyday living

"A kiss can be a comma, a question mark or an exclamation point. That's basic spelling that every woman ought to know."

Mistinguett

"We owe almost all our knowledge, not to those who have agreed, but to those who have differed."

Charles Caleb Colton

"To know that we know what we know, and that we do not know what we do not know, that is true knowledge."

Henry David Thoreau

"As we acquire more knowledge, things do not become more comprehensible, but more mysterious."

Albert Schweitzer

𝕶

Name

✉

☎

Name

✉

☎

Name

✉

☎

Name

✉

☎

Name

✉

☎

Name

✉

☎

IN THE KITCHEN ~ INTERNATIONAL RECIPES

FROM HUNGARY

STUFFED MUSHROOMS WITH EGER SAUCE
Ingredients

Mushroom caps	Breadcrumbs
1 tbsp lemon juice	1/2 tsp salt
Goose liver paté (or similar)	Deep fat or oil for frying
Beaten egg	

For the Eger (red wine) Sauce:

1 tbsp redcurrant jelly	1/4 pint red wine or port wine
1/4 pint lamb gravy or stock	

Method

To make the sauce, heat all ingredients together until the jelly has melted. Boil mushroom caps in water with salt and lemon juice until just tender. Stuff with paté and sandwich 2 caps together. Coat with eggs then breadcrumbs, then deep fry for a few minutes until lightly browned. Drain and serve immediately with red wine sauce.

STUFFED PANCAKES HORTO BAGY STYLE
Ingredients

Veal stew with paprika	Cream and sour cream to taste
Pancakes	

Method

Prepare veal stew with paprika. Mince cooked meat and use to stuff pancakes. Pile into ovenproof dish and cover with sauce made from stew gravy, cream and sour cream. Serve hot.

HUNGARIAN APPLE PIE
Ingredients

1 lb cooking apples	1 egg, separated
4 oz butter	2 oz ground almonds
1-2 tbsp milk	Strawberry jam
6 oz plain flour	

Method

Stew apples in as little water as possible. Sieve flour, rub in butter and mix to a dough with egg yolk and milk. Leave in cool place for 30 mins. Line 7-inch sandwich tin with half the pastry and partly blind bake for 10 mins. Mix ground almonds with sugar. Spread pastry with jam and cover with half the almond mixture. Fold stiffly whisked egg white into apple and put in pie tin. Sprinkle rest of sugar and almond mixture on top and cover with remaining pastry. Brush with milk and sprinkle with sugar. Bake in a hot oven for 25-30 mins. Serve with cream.

EVERYDAY THOUGHTS
for everyday living

"The fruits of labour are the
sweetest of all pleasures."

Luc De Vauvenargues

"Laughter has no foreign accent."

Paul Lowney

"The most wasted day is that in
which we have not laughed."

Chamfort

"Learning is ever young, even in
old age."

Aeschylus

"Learn as though you would never
be able to master it; hold it as
though you would be in fear of
losing it."

Confucius

Addresses • Addresses • Addresses • Addresses • Addresses • Addresses • Addresses

Name

✉

☎

Name

✉

☎

Name

✉

☎

Name

✉

☎

Name

✉

☎

Name

✉

☎

IN THE KITCHEN ~ INTERNATIONAL RECIPES

FROM SCOTLAND

Scotch Broth
Ingredients

1 lb boiling beef/neck of mutton	2 carrots
4 pints water	2 leeks
2 tbsp barley (pearl)	3 tbsp swede, diced
1 tsp salt	1 onion
2 tbsp yellow split peas	1/2 small cabbage
2 tbsp dried green peas	1 dsp finely chopped parsley

Method

Put the water, salt, peas, washed pearl barley and meat into a large saucepan. Slowly bring to the boil. Skim. Dice vegetables, shred the cabbage and add. Bring back to the boil and simmer for about 2 hours until the meat is cooked and the peas tender. Add parsley, salt and pepper.

Everyday Scotch Haggis
Ingredients

1/2 lb ox liver	2 pinches black pepper
4 oz shredded suet	1 teacup water
1 onion	3/4 dsp salt
4 oz oatmeal, pinhead	

Method

In a small saucepan put liver, onion and water. Boil for 15 minutes. Toast the oatmeal for a few minutes in the oven until it is light brown. Mince the liver and onion. Mix everything together with the liquid and seasoning. Serve with swedes and mashed potatoes.

Petticoat Tails
Ingredients

12 oz margarine/butter	9 oz icing sugar
18 oz plain flour	1 tbsp castor sugar

Method

Cream the butter and sift in the icing sugar. Beat the flour in with the icing sugar, adding sufficient water to make a firm dough. Roll the dough out thinly into a large square. Cut it into 2-inch triangles. Place the triangles on a greased baking sheet and bake at 325°F (or equivalent temperature) for 30 minutes. Remove from oven and dust with castor sugar while they are still hot. Leave the triangles on the tray to cool.

EVERYDAY THOUGHTS
for everyday living

"We make a living by what we get, but
we make a life by what we give."

Norman MacEwan

"It is not the years in your life but the
life in your years that counts!"

Adlai Stevenson

"The love we give away is the
only love we keep."

Elbert Hubbard

"Treasure the love you receive
above all. It will survive long
after your gold and good health
have vanished."

Og Mandino

"Who, being loved, is poor?"

Oscar Wilde

Name
✉

☎
Name
✉

☎
Name
✉

☎
Name
✉

☎
Name
✉

☎
Name
✉

☎

USEFUL INFORMATION

TEMPERATURE

F'heit	22°F	32°F	41°F	59°F	68°F	86°F
Celsius	-5°C	0°C	5°C	15°C	20°C	30°C

Conversion Formulae

$$C = \frac{5}{9} (F - 32)$$
$$F = \frac{9}{5} (C + 32)$$

ROMAN NUMERALS

I	=	1		XVI	=	16
II	=	2		XVII	=	17
III	=	3		XVIII	=	18
IV	=	4		XIX	=	19
V	=	5		XX	=	20
VI	=	6		XXX	=	30
VII	=	7		XL	=	40
VIII	=	8		L	=	50
IX	=	9		LX	=	60
X	=	10		LXX	=	70
XI	=	11		LXXX	=	80
XII	=	12		XC	=	90
XIII	=	13		C	=	100
XIV	=	14		D	=	500
XV	=	15		M	=	1000

WIND SPEEDS

1	7 mph light wind
2	11 mph light breeze
3	16 mph gentle breeze
4	20 mph moderate breeze
5	25 mph fresh breeze
6	30 mph strong breeze
7	35 mph moderate gale
8	45 mph fresh gale
9	50 mph strong gale
10	60 mph whole gale
11	70 mph storm
12	80 mph hurricane

~ INTERNATIONAL PAPER SIZES (A SERIES) ~

SIZE	MILIMETRES	INCHES
A0	841 x 1189	33.1 x 46.8
A1	594 x 841	23.4 x 33.1
A2	420 x 594	16.5 x 23.4
A3	297 x 420	11.7 x 16.5
A4	210 x 297	8.3 x 11.7
A5	148 x 210	5.8 x 8.3
A6	105 x 148	4.1 x 5.8
A7	74 x 105	2.9 x 4.1

EVERYDAY THOUGHTS
for everyday living

"Marriage is an empty box.
It remains empty unless you put
in more than you take out."

Author Unidentified

"Married couples who love each
other tell each other a thousand
things without talking."

Chinese Proverb

"Often the difference between a
successful marriage and a mediocre
one consists of leaving about three
or four things a day unsaid."

Harlan Miller

"Marriage is three parts love and
seven parts forgiveness of sins."

Langdon Mitchell

"There is no more lovely, friendly
and charming relationship,
communion or company than a
good marriage."

Martin Luther

𝔐

Name

✉

☎

Name

✉

☎

Name

✉

☎

Name

✉

☎

Name

✉

☎

Name

✉

☎

Name

✉

☎

USEFUL INFORMATION

~ METRIC CONVERSIONS ~

Metric Conversions	multiply by	Metric Conversions	multiply by
acres to hectares	0.4047	ounces to grammes	28.35
cubic inches to cubic centimetres	16.39	pounds to kilogrammes	0.4536
cubic feet to cubic metres	0.02832	pounds to grammes	453.6
cubic yards to cubic metres	0.7646	square inches to square centimetres	6.452
cubic inches to litres	0.01639	square feet to square metres	0.0929
feet to metres	0.3048	square yards to square metres	0.8361
gallons to litres	4.546	square miles to square kilometres	2.590
grains to grammes	0.0648	tons to kilogrammes	1016.00
inches to centimetres	2.540	yards to metres	0.9144
miles to kilometres	1.609		

~ CLOTHING SIZES ~

SHIRTS (COLLAR)

Inches	14½	15	15½	16	16½	17	17½
Centimetres	37	38	39-40	41	42	43	44

MEN'S JACKETS (CHEST)

Inches	36	38	40	42	44	46
Centimetres	91	97	102	107	112	117
Continental	46	48	50	52	54	56

WOMEN'S DRESSES & SUITS

Inches	34	36	38	40	42	44
Centimetres	86	91	97	102	107	112

TROUSERS WAIST

Inches	30	32	34	36	38	40	42
Centimetres	76	81	86	91	97	102	107

SHOES

British Sizes	2	3	4	5	6	7
Continental	34	35.5	37	38	39.5	40.5
British Sizes	8	9	10	11	12	
Continental	42	43	44.5	45.5	47	

SOCKS

British Sizes	9½	10	10½	11	11½
Continental	38-39	39-40	40-41	41-42	42-43

EVERYDAY THOUGHTS
for everyday living

"Memory is the treasury and
guardian of all things."

Cicero

"God gave us memories that we
might have roses in December."

James M Barrie

"The greatest mistake you can make in
life is to be continually fearing you will
make one."

Elbert Hubbard

"He who makes no mistakes
never makes anything."

English Proverb

"The shortest mistakes are always
the best."

J.B. Molière

𝕸

Name

✉

☎

Name

✉

☎

Name

✉

☎

Name

✉

☎

Name

✉

☎

Name

✉

☎

WEIGHTS & MEASURES

LENGTH

1 centimetre (cm)	=	0.3937 in		
1 metre (m)	=	100 cm	=	1.0936 yds
1 kilometre (km)	=	1000 m	=	0,6214 mile
1 inch	=	2.5400 cm		
1 yard	=	36 in	=	0.9144 m
1 mile	=	1760 yds	=	1.6093 km

AREA

1 sq metre (m²)	=	10 000 cm²	=	1.1960 sq yds
1 hectare (ha)	=	10 000 m²	=	2.4711 acres
1 sq km (km²)	=	100 hectares	=	0.3861 sq mile
1 sq yd	=	9 sq ft	=	0.8361 m²
1 acre	=	4840 sq yds	=	4046.9 m²

CAPACITY

1 cu dm (dm³)	=	1000 cm³	=	0.0353 cu ft
1 cu metre (m³)	=	1000 dm³	=	1.3080 cu yds
1 litre	=	1 dm²	=	0.2200 gallon
1 cu yd	=	27 cu ft	=	0.7646 m³
1 pint	=	4 gills	=	0.5683 litre
1 gallon	=	8 pints	=	4.5461 litres

WEIGHT

1 gramme (g)	=	1000 mg	=	0.3535 oz
1 kilogramme (kg)	=	1000 g	=	2.2046 lb
1 tonne (t)	=	1000 kg	=	0.9842 ton
1 ounce	=	437.5 grains	=	28.350 g
1 pound	=	16 oz	=	0.4536 kg
1 ton	=	2240 pounds	=	1.0161 tonnes

EVERYDAY THOUGHTS
for everyday living

"What's in a name?
That which we call a rose,
By any other name would smell as
sweet."

Shakespeare: Romeo & Juliet

"A nation reveals itself not only by the
men it produces but also by the men it
honours, the men it remembers."

John F Kennedy

"Those things are better which are
perfected by nature than those
which are finished by art."

Cicero

"God made the beauties of nature like
a child playing in the sand."

Ascribed to Apollonius of Tyana

"Better is a neighbour that is near than
a brother far off."

Proverbs 27:10

N

Name _____
✉ _____
_____
☎ _____
Name _____
✉ _____
_____
☎ _____
Name _____
✉ _____
_____
☎ _____
Name _____
✉ _____
_____
☎ _____
Name _____
✉ _____
_____
☎ _____
Name _____
✉ _____
_____
☎ _____

Addresses • Addresses • Addresses • Addresses • Addresses • Addresses • Addresses

ANIMAL HAIR

Use sellotape to remove animal hair from clothes, furniture etc. Simply wrap the sellotape around your fingers (sticky side outward) and rub over the hairs.

ANTS

You can discourage ants in the house by sprinkling bicarbonate of soda or powdered borax of cloves on shelves and in drawers.

ASH

Do not empty these into a wastepaper basket as they can easily start a fire. A large tin is much more suitable. To prevent cigarette ends from burning in an ashtray and to reduce the smell of stale tobacco, coat the bottom of the ashtray with baking powder.

BAKING TINS

To discourage a new baking tin from rusting, rub it inside and out with lard and place it in an oven at moderate heat for forty-five minutes. When cool wipe thoroughly with a paper towel. To remove rust from tinware rub with half a raw potato that has been dipped in scouring powder. Rinse and then dry - ideally in an oven.

BALL POINT PENS

If a ballpoint pen doesn't work try warming the point gently with a match or by pouring boiling water over it.

BARBECUE

To maximise the heat line your barbecue with tin-foil, shiny side up. Use left over brewed coffee to clean the barbecue set.

BATHS

If you have unsightly stains on your bath or wash basin due to a dripping tap, try rubbing with a paste made of lemon juice and salt and rinsing well. Failing this, try rubbing them with a toothbrush using a paste of cream of tartar and peroxide and then rinsing.

BOOKS

To keep your books in good condition do not place them tight against a wall, but leave a couple of centimetres gap to enable the air to circulate around them. Also, make sure they are kept upright and not leaning at an angle as this would be bad for their bindings.

If the pages of a book are torn slightly, place them in position and smear lightly with the white of an egg, leaving the book open to dry.

Carpet tape is useful when trying to repair the spine of a book.

BOTTLES

Stick an adhesive plaster over the cork of the bottle containing liquid when packing to help prevent accidents. It is also advisable to pack bottles between soft items.

Bottles are best emptied by shaking them in a circular motion.

EVERYDAY THOUGHTS
for everyday living

"When your neighbour's house is afire,
your own property is at stake."

Horace

"Night is the mother of counsels."

George Herbert

"The day is done, and the darkness
Falls from the wings of Night,
As a feather is wafted downward
From an eagle in his flight."

Longfellow

"Be noble! and the nobleness that lies
In other men, sleeping, but never dead,
Will rise in majesty to meet thine own."

James Russell Lowell

"How sad would be November if we
had no knowledge of the spring!"

Edwin Way Teale

N

Name
✉

☎
Name
✉

☎
Name
✉

☎
Name
✉

☎
Name
✉

☎
Name
✉

☎

If you find difficulty unscrewing a bottle or container give a firm tap to the bottom of the container.

Remove strong odours from bottles by filling them with a mixture of cold  water and four teaspoons of dry mustard and leaving them to stand for a least half a day before rinsing well.

BREAD BOARDS
If your wooden bread board is warped, place it on a flat surface and cover it with a wet cloth, leaving it for at least 24 hours.

BROOMS
When a broom handle does not fit anymore then wrap with adhesive tape and screw the handle back into the socket. This should help keep it in place.

CANDLES
To increase the life span of candles keep them in the freezer for a few hours before use.

To make candles fit into candle sticks dip the end in hot water until it is soft enough to fit into the required size.

Wash the candle stick holder in soapy water with a few drops of ammonia to remove the wax.

CAR
To prevent bumping your car in a tight garage attach an old tyre to the wall.

To clean a very dirty car use a mixture of methylated spirit and water (1 unit of methylated spirit to 8 units of water). Do not rinse. This should leave your car shining.

CARPETS
When choosing a carpet ask to see it flat on the floor. The colour might look quite different when the carpet is displayed rolled vertically.

To restore the life to carpet pile which has been flattened by furniture legs, place several layers of wet cloth onto the area. Then hold a hot iron lightly on top of the cloth. The steam should bring back the bounce to the carpet which can then be fluffed up using a nail brush.

CHINA
Protect your best china plates from chips and cracks by alternating them with paper plates or corrugated paper when storing them or when packing them.

COOKING SMELLS
Get rid of unwanted cooking smells by boiling one teaspoon of ground cinnamon or ground cloves in a $\frac{1}{4}$ litre of water for fifteen minutes.

CORK
Cork expands. If it does not fit back into the bottle then place it in boiling water for a few minutes until it becomes soft. It will then fit easily back into the bottle.

CRYSTAL
To give a real sparkle to your crystal add a few drops of ammonia to the washing water and vinegar to the rinsing water.

EVERYDAY THOUGHTS
for everyday living

"The woman who obeys her
husband rules him."

Spanish Proverb

"An old man loved is winter with
flowers."

German Proverb

"Our opinions are less important
than the spirit and temper with
which they possess us, and even
good opinions are worth very little
unless we hold them in a broad,
intelligent, and spacious way."

John Morley

"Every man values himself more than
all the rest of men, but he always
values others' opinions of himself
more than his own."

Marcus Aurelius

Addresses • Addresses • Addresses • Addresses • Addresses • Addresses • Addresses

Name
✉

☎

Name
✉

☎

Name
✉

☎

Name
✉

☎

Name
✉

☎

Name
✉

☎

HANDY HINTS

DAMPNESS
To determine whether dampness is caused by condensation or is coming from outside, attach a piece of silver foil to the affected area. If moisture appears on the front surface then this is caused by condensation in the room and you should look for better ways of ventilating the room. If, however, the foil is wet on the side of the wall, the damp comes from the outside and you should seek professional help.

DECORATING
When you have decorated a room, make sure you keep a note of the number of rolls of wallpaper or tins of paint that you used, so that when you come to redecorating, you will know exactly what you need.

DISHWASHERS
Pour 4 heaped tablespoons of bicarbonate of soda through the bottom rack of your dishwasher and put it on the rinse cycle to refresh the smell.

DOORS
Silence a creaky door by rubbing soap along the hinges.

DRAWERS
If you have trouble opening tight fitting drawers, rub soap or candle wax along the upper edges to lubricate them.

DRILLING
To stop the drill from slipping when drilling a hole into metal or ceramic tiles, cover the mark with adhesive tape, drill through it and then remove the tape.

When drilling into the ceiling, drill through the base of an old squash bottle or transparent plastic container and this will catch the chips and stop them from going into your eyes.

EASTER EGGS
Use natural products to dye Easter eggs: beetroot juice will make a red dye, saffron will give you yellow, and spinach juice will produce a green colour.

EGG BOXES
Cardboard or fibre egg boxes are ideal for growing seeds. When the shoots are ready for planting, just bury the entire tray. The roots will not be disturbed and the tray will disintegrate after a while.

ELECTRIC-WIRE
When fitting a plug it is often difficult to cut the rubber which encompasses the wire without cutting the copper thread. If you warm the rubber with a match you will be able to strip it very easily with your fingers.

ENAMEL
If your enamel is cracked and the cracks become dirty, make a thick paste of French chalk and water and coat the enamel with it. Leave it until the paste dries out and begins to crack and then brush off. Repeat until the cracks come clean.

ERASERS
Washing-up liquid effectively cleans dirty erasers.

FELT-TIPPED PENS
If your felt-tip pen seems to have run out, try

EVERYDAY THOUGHTS
for everyday living

"One often contradicts an opinion when it is really only the tone in which it has been presented that is unsympathetic."

Nietzsche

"When we stop to think, we often miss our opportunity."

Publilius Syrus

"A wise man will make more opportunities than he finds."

Francis Bacon

"An optimist sees an opportunity in every calamity: a pessimist sees a calamity in every opportunity."

Author Unidentified

"Originality does not consist in saying what no one has ever said before, but in saying exactly what you think yourself."

James Fitz-James Stephen

Addresses • Addresses • Addresses • Addresses • Addresses • Addresses • Addresses

Name

✉

☎

Name

✉

☎

Name

✉

☎

Name

✉

☎

Name

✉

☎

Name

✉

☎

dipping the tip in a little vinegar - this should give it a new lease of life. Store felt-tip pens tip downwards with the cap on so that they are always ready to use.

FINGER NAILS
If you want to take care of your nails, never cut them with scissors as this can cause them to split. File them with an emery board - from the sides up to the tip (and never in a see-saw movement) - as this is softer than a metal file.

FIREPLACES
If you are lighting a fire in a chimney which has not been used for some time and which may be damp, first burn a creased sheet of newspaper in the grate. This should remove the moisture from the chimney and help you get the best out of the fireplace.

When burning a fire, do not burn coloured magazines or newspaper as the coloured ink will give off some lead vapour when burning.

FLIES
A pleasant way of discouraging flies is by placing cotton wool balls sprinkled with a few drops of lavender oil on saucers around the room. Basil or mint grown in pots on the windowsill or in a window box is also a sweet smelling way of deterring flies.

FLOORS
Talcum powder sprinkled between floorboards will help to stop them from squeaking.

FLOWERS
If you are picking flowers from the garden, do

not do it during the warmest part of the day as the flowers will not last long. Pick them in the early morning or early evening if you want them to last longer.

FOIL
Wrap food tightly in kitchen foil for storing but loosely for cooking.

FRAMING
Insert kitchen foil behind the picture when framing to prevent damage from damp.

FREEZER
When you have defrosted your freezer rub the inside with glycerine. Next time you come to defrost it you should find that the ice will come away easily.

To stop packages from sticking to the freezer walls or bottom, do not put them straight back into the freezer after defrosting but leave the freezer empty for half an hour first.

FURNITURE
When it is exposed to direct sunlight, polished furniture will permanently lose its veneer. To

EVERYDAY THOUGHTS
for everyday living

"If we live in peace ourselves, we
in turn may bring peace to others.
A peaceable man does more good
than a learned one."

Thomas À Kempis

"Perfection is attained by slow degrees;
it requires the hand of time."

Voltaire

"By perseverance the snail reached
the Ark."

C H Spurgeon

"Philosophy triumphs easily over past,
and over future evils, but present evils
triumph over philosophy."

La Rochefoucauld

"The entire world would perish,
if pity were not to limit anger."

Seneca the Elder

Name ✉

☎

Name ✉

☎

Name ✉

☎

Name ✉

☎

Name ✉

☎

Name ✉

☎

avoid lasting damage, either position the piece of furniture elsewhere, or keep it covered with a cloth.

FUSES
Keep a torch and a card of fuse wire beside the fuse box in case of an emergency.

GARDEN TOOLS
To remove rust from your garden tools use wire wool dipped in turpentine.

GARLIC
To remove the smell of garlic from your breath try chewing some fresh mint, a coffee bean, a stalk of parsley or celery or some cardamom seeds!

GIFT WRAP
When you are wrapping large numbers of presents, at Christmas for example or at a children's party, try using attractive leftover wallpaper which makes a far cheaper alternative to gift wrap.

GLASSES
If two glasses have stuck together and you are finding it difficult to separate them, stand the bottom glass in hot (not boiling) water and fill the top one with cold water. This should cause them to separate without damaging them.

To get rid of small chips around the rim of a glass, rub them with fine sandpaper until smooth.

Stand a silver spoon in a glass or jar to prevent it from cracking when boiling water is poured into it.

GLUE
Fit a piece of candle on the top of a glue bottle and use it as a stopper to close the bottle. As glue does not stick to candle wax you should no longer have any problems when you come to open it.

GRASS
To prevent grass from growing between the cracks in your paving stones or path, sprinkle salt in them, or pour on very salted boiling water.

GREENFLY
You can help to discourage greenfly by planting garlic around the plants that attract the greenfly. When the garlic starts sprouting, keep the shoots cut back.

GUTTERS
A piece of chicken wire placed over the top of your gutter will effectively prevent falling leaves from blocking it.

HANGERS
If you have a skirt without any loops and are short of special hangers, wind a rubber band around each end of an ordinary hanger to prevent the skirt from falling off, or put two clothes pegs on an ordinary wire hanger.

EVERYDAY THOUGHTS
for everyday living

"Poetry is the opening and closing of a door, leaving those who look through to guess about what is seen during a moment."

Carl Sandburg

"It is not the man who has little, but he who desires more, that is poor."

Seneca

"The sole advantage of power is that you can do more good."

Baltasar Gracián

"Prejudice is the child of ignorance."

William Hazlitt

"Problems are opportunities in work clothes."

Henry Kaiser

"To the pure all things are pure."

Titus 1:15

P

Name

✉

☎

Name

✉

☎

Name

✉

☎

Name

✉

☎

Name

✉

☎

Name

✉

☎

HARD WATER DEPOSITS

If you find hard water deposits in jugs, bottles, vases or glasses etc., fill the object with malt vinegar and leave it for a few hours or as long as necessary. Then rub off with a fine wire scouring pad and rinse thoroughly. The vinegar can be reused.

HOSE

To make the hose fit easily onto the tap rub the inside of the hose with some soap. The soap will quickly dry when the hose is fitted.

HOT-WATER BOTTLES

When filling a hot-water bottle lie it flat on its back holding the neck upright. This will prevent the water splashing due to air-bubbles in the bottle. Add a little salt to the water to keep it warm longer.

INSECTS

By hanging a fresh bunch of stinging nettles in front of any open windows or doors, you can discourage flies and wasps from invading your house.

IRONING

Starch can be removed from the bottom of your iron by sprinkling a piece of paper with some fine kitchen salt and rubbing the iron over it until the base becomes smooth again,

or by rubbing the base with half a lemon dipped in fine kitchen salt.

A few drops of your favourite toilet water mixed with the water in the iron or sprinkled first on the ironing board will perfume your linen lightly.

IVORY

Very dirty ivory can be cleaned by leaving the item to soak for a few hours in milk and then washing it with warm soapy water.

To keep small pieces of ivory white, place them in the direct sunlight. Alternatively, to colour a piece of ivory which looks too new, dip it in strong tea or coffee. Do not leave it to soak but keep dipping it in and out until the desired effect is reached. Dry and polish.

JARS

Leave a few drops of bleach in a glass jar to remove strong fish or pickle smells. You will have to leave the bleach in for at least twelve hours.

If you make some small holes in the lid of a jam jar or other glass screw-topped jar with a nail or skewer, you can use it as a cheap flour dredger or as a water sprinkler when ironing.

EVERYDAY THOUGHTS
for everyday living

"Quarrels would not last long if the fault was only on one side."

La Rochefoucauld

"The second word makes the quarrel."

Japanese Proverb

"Most quarrels amplify a misunderstanding."

André Gide

"You can make up a quarrel but it will always show where it was patched."

Edgar Watson Howe

"Better is a handful with quietness, than both the hands full with travails and vexation of spirit."

Ecclesiastes 4:6

"No wealth is like the quiet mind."

Anon

Addresses • Addresses • Addresses • Addresses • Addresses • Addresses • Addresses • Addresses • Addresses

Q

Name

✉

☎

Name

✉

☎

Name

✉

☎

Name

✉

☎

Name

✉

☎

Name

✉

☎

HANDY HINTS

JAR LABELS
Do not label your jars until the contents have cooled, otherwise the labels will come unstuck.

JEWELLERY
If you want to give a quick shine to gold jewellery, rub the item with a ball of soft bread. Likewise if you want an item of silver jewellery to shine, rub it with half a lemon and then rinse before drying.

To loosen or remove a ring which is stuck on your finger, wash your hands with soap and water and try to take the ring off while the soap is still on your hands.

KETTLES
Place a marble in your kettle to prevent it from furring. To defur a kettle fill it with water and put the kettle in your freezer. When it defrosts the ice will pull the fur of the sides. Alternatively, pour in a small quantity of vinegar (enough to cover the element where applicable), bring it to the boil then agitate it. Leave it to cool and then rinse thoroughly. It may be necessary to repeat these processes several times.

KEYS
Covering a rusty key with turpentine and leaving it to soak for a couple of hours before rubbing and drying it should bring its shine back.

KNITWEAR
To prevent your knitwear from stretching when you are washing it in the washing machine, place it first inside a pillowcase.

LEATHER SHOES
When drying leather shoes or boots, never be tempted to do so quickly in front of the fire as the leather will harden and will be more likely to crack.

LIDS
If you cannot unscrew a lid, place the jar in boiling water for a few minutes. It should then become loose and easy to unscrew.

LIGHT BULBS
You can delicately scent your room by rubbing just a few drops of your favourite perfume onto a light bulb. A pleasant smell will be emitted when the light bulb is on.

LINEN
To prevent fine linen which is not in constant use from becoming discoloured and yellow, wrap it in blue tissue paper.

LINOLEUM
Unsightly black marks on linoleum floors can be removed quite simply by using a pencil-eraser. A few drops of paraffin in the water when washing will help make linoleum shine.

LIPSTICK
When you are testing a lipstick for colour, the best place to try it is on the cushion of your finger, where the skin is pinkish, like the lips.

LOCKS
When you cannot get your key to turn in a lock and it seems to be jammed, rub the key with vaseline, or, failing that, butter or margarine. This should help to ease the lock.

EVERYDAY THOUGHTS
for everyday living

"It is reason that produces
everything: virtue, genius, wit, talent,
and taste. What is virtue? Reason in
practise. Talent? Reason enveloped
in glory. Wit? Reason which is
chastely expressed. Taste is nothing
else than reason delicately put in
force, and genius is reason in its
most sublime form."

M J de Chenier

"Opportunities flit by while we sit
regretting the chances we have lost,
and the happiness that comes to us we
heed not, because of the happiness
that is gone."

Jerome K Jerome

"To regret deeply is to live afresh."

Thoreau

"Work is the price which is paid
for reputation."

Baltasar Gracian

Addresses • Addresses • Addresses • Addresses • Addresses • Addresses • Addresses

Name

Name

Name

Name

Name

Name

Name

A lubricating effect can also be achieved by rubbing a key all over with the lead of a pencil and working it in the lock several times. This will help to keep the lock in good working order.

MATS

You can help to prevent the edges of a mat from curling up by pasting some very thick starch along the edge and then ironing over some brown paper with a fairly hot iron.

MATCHES

A damp match can be made to light by coating the tip in nail varnish. You do not even have to wait for the nail varnish to dry before striking it. An alternative is to rub it against the bristles of a brush.

MICROWAVE OVENS

You can help to remove stubborn and unpleasant cooking smells from inside a microwave oven by placing a teacup containing 3 parts water to 1 part lemon juice or vinegar inside it and cooking for eight to ten minutes on the lowest setting. Wipe the oven dry afterwards.

MIRRORS

If, before you run your bath, you rub the bathroom mirror with a few drops of shampoo, this will help prevent it from steaming up.

MOTHS

Small muslin bags filled with aromatic plants placed in your wardrobe and drawers will deter moths and will make your clothes smell nice at the same time.

NAILS

When hammering small nails use a hairslide as a holder or stick plasticine over the area you wish to hammer the nail into. This will hold the nail in position and will protect your fingers.

To prevent cracking the plaster when hammering in nails, first stick a piece of sellotape or masking tape to the wall, then hammer the nail in through the tape.

When trying to remove a nail which has been painted over, first soften the paint by holding a lighted match just below it, being careful not to burn the wall.

NAIL VARNISH

You can keep the top of a bottle of nail varnish from sticking and becoming difficult to open by spreading a little vaseline on the grooves.

Storing the bottle in the fridge will prevent the nail varnish from getting a sticky consistency and it will also help the varnish to last longer.

If the varnish thickens, it can be brought back to a better consistency by adding just a few drops of nail varnish remover.

NEWSPAPER

Roll a newspaper into a long thin tube, knotted in the middle, when you are lighting a fire.

OVENS

Next time you clean your oven, after cleaning and drying it rub it all over with a paste made of bicarbonate of soda and water. This should make it easier to wipe clean next time around.

EVERYDAY THOUGHTS
for everyday living

"Respect a man, he will do the more."

James Howell

"If you have some respect for people as they are, you can be more effective in helping them to become better than they are."

John W Gardner

"He that can take rest is greater than he that can take cities."

Benjamin Franklin

"It is better to be miserable and rich than it is to be miserable and poor."

Author Unidentified

"The rich man is not one who is in possession of much, but one who gives much."

St. John Chrysostom

Name

✉

☎

Name

✉

☎

Name

✉

☎

Name

✉

☎

Name

✉

☎

Name

✉

☎

ℜ

HANDY HINTS

PAINT

When selecting a single colour for the walls of a room, always choose one a shade lighter than you want, as paint tends to look darker once it is on the wall.

To keep the top of a paint tin clean, when painting place a paper plate over the top of the tin with the middle cut out. This way all the drops will land on the plate and not on the tin, and the plate can simply be discarded after you have finished painting.

The strong smell left in your house after you have been painting can be avoided by using a mixture of one tablespoon of vanilla essence to two pints paint when you are painting. Or while painting, try adding a couple of tablespoons of ammonia to one or two shallow containers of water placed in the room you are working on - this should stop the smell from spreading around the house.

PAINTBRUSHES

Dried out brushes can be restored to life by immersing them in hot vinegar, while errant bristles can be encouraged to return to their proper place by spraying the brush head with hairspray, smoothing and leaving to dry.

PAINT TUBES

To get a stubborn cap off a small tube of artist's paint, try holding a lighted match under the cap for just a few seconds.

PAN

Before using a new pan, boil some vinegar in it for a few minutes to prevent food from sticking.

PARCELS

When you are wrapping a parcel using string, first dip the string in warm water and then tie the knot. When the string dries it will shrink, leaving you with a tight knot.

PIANOS

Do not place a lot of books or ornaments on the top of a piano as it will deaden the tone. If a piano key stays down when it is struck then it is a sign of dampness.

Ivory keys will become yellowed more quickly if the lid of the piano is kept down, as ivory yellows more in the dark.

PINS

If you keep a small magnet in your pin box, then if you drop it the keys will be more likely to cluster around the magnet, making it easier to collect them.

PLASTIC BOTTLES

For easier and more compact disposal of your

EVERYDAY THOUGHTS
for everyday living

"Silence is as full of potential
wisdom and wit as the unhewn
marble of great sculpture."

Aldous Huxley

"The art of art, the glory of
expression and the sunshine of
the light of letters, is simplicity."

Walt Whitman

"Sincerity is the highest
compliment you can pay."

Ralph Waldo Emerson

"Sorrow is better than fear . . .
Fear is a journey, a terrible
journey, but sorrow is at least an
arriving."

Alan Paton: Cry the Beloved Country

"Our joys as winged dreams do fly,
Why then should sorrow last?"

Thomas Percy

Addresses • Addresses • Addresses • Addresses • Addresses • Addresses • Addresses

Name _____ 𝕾

✉ _____

☎ _____

Name _____

✉ _____

☎ _____

Name _____

✉ _____

☎ _____

Name _____

✉ _____

☎ _____

Name _____

✉ _____

☎ _____

Name _____

✉ _____

☎ _____

plastic bottles, pour a small quantity of boiling water into the bottle. This will cause it to become soft and to collapse, making it easier to crush the bottle in your hands.

PLASTICINE
A quick substitute for plasticine for children to play with can be made by making a dough with flour, water and salt. This can be coloured with a little paprika or mustard powder to make it more attractive, and it will stay soft if stored in a sealed plastic bag.

If you do not want to use a trellis and yet still wish your ivy to grow up the wall, encourage it by sticking it to the wall from time to time with plasticine.

PLASTERS
If you find removing sticking plaster from your skin painful, first rub baby oil over the plaster. You should find it easier to remove.

REFRIGERATORS
A piece of charcoal placed inside your fridge will absorb the smells of strong food such as fish and cheese and will only need to be replaced every five-to-six months.

If your fridge is noisy it could simply be that it is not standing on a level surface.

RUBBER GLOVES
As hands sweat a lot in rubber gloves, they may become damp and smell unpleasant. Avoid this by dusting the inside of the gloves with talc when you use them and by washing the insides from time to time. It will also help

if you dry the gloves inside out after you have used them.

RUBBISH
To keep dogs and cats away from your rubbish sprinkle pure ammonia over the bags.

RUGS
To keep a rug from slipping or wrinkling on a carpet or shiny floor, stick some plastic stick-ons, commonly used for the bath, on the underside of the rug. Alternatively, you could sew or glue pieces of carpet, pile downwards, under the corners of the rug.

RUST
Rust on utensils can be removed by rubbing the stains with a cork dipped in olive oil. Rust stains on metal will sometimes disappear when rubbed with half a raw onion.

SCISSORS
To sharpen your scissors cut a sheet of emery paper into small pieces.

SHINE
Black or dark coloured clothes often become shiny with wear. This can be alleviated by brushing the shiny part with black coffee - half a teacup of strong black coffee to half a teacup of water. Then press with a cloth. Alternatively, you could rub the article with a piece of clean cloth dampened with turpentine or white spirit. The smell will soon disappear.

SHOES
When buying shoes, wait until the afternoon. Your feet tend to be relaxed first thing in the

EVERYDAY THOUGHTS
for everyday living

"It is excellent
To have a giant's strength, but it is
tyrannous
To use it like a giant."

Shakespeare: Measure for Measure

"The true measure of success is not
what you have, but what you can do
without."

Author Unidentified

"He has achieved success who
has lived well, laughed often and
loved much."

Bessie Anderson Stanley

"Know how sublime a thing it is
to suffer and be strong."

Longfellow

"Pity may represent little more than the
impersonal concern which prompts the
mailing of a cheque, but true sympathy
is the personal concern which
demands the giving of one's soul."

Martin Luther King

S

Name _____

✉ _____

☎ _____

Name _____

✉ _____

☎ _____

Name _____

✉ _____

☎ _____

Name _____

✉ _____

☎ _____

Name _____

✉ _____

☎ _____

Name _____

✉ _____

☎ _____

morning after a night's sleep but may swell slightly during the day, so if you buy your shoes early in the morning you may find that they pinch you in the evening.

Remove the odour from smelly shoes by sprinkling a tablespoon of bicarbonate of soda inside each shoe and leaving it overnight.

When drying wet shoes, stuff them with newspaper to help them keep their shape.

SHOWER CURTAINS
To prevent mildew on your cloth shower curtains, soak them for half an hour in a strong solution of salted water, then hang them up to dry. Rubbing the curtains with bicarbonate of soda will also help remove mildew.

SLUGS
One of the less offensive ways of killing slugs is by distributing bran around the garden, which they are attracted to but which kills them. (The bran will also attract snails, who will assemble around it making it easy to collect them).

Alternatively, you can entice the slugs with a glass of beer left in the garden overnight.

SMOKE
To prevent a room from becoming smoky when people are smoking in it, try lighting a few candles, or strat-

egically arrange a few small containers filled with vinegar. This should help to eliminate the smoke from the room.

STAINS
When removing a stain, work from the edge of the stain inwards. This will help prevent the stain from spreading.

STAMPS
When you wish to remove an unused stamp from an envelope without damaging it, submerge the corner of the envelope with the stamp on it in boiling water for a few minutes. The stamp should then come off easily and can be left to dry.

Another method is to wet the back of the stamp inside the envelope with lighter fluid.

STICKY LABELS
Stubborn sticky labels on glass or china can be removed with nail-varnish remover, cooking oil, turpentine or white spirit.

THERMOS FLASKS
To clean a stained thermos flask put three tablespoons of bicarbonate of soda into it and fill up with warm water. Agitate it and leave to stand for quarter of an hour. Then rinse and leave to dry.

Stubborn coffee smells and stains can be eliminated by pouring in a cup of boiling water and one tablespoon of raw rice. Shake the flask for a few minutes and then rinse.

If you will not be using your flask for a while,

EVERYDAY THOUGHTS
for everyday living

"Waste not fresh tears over old griefs."

Euripides

"There's no seeing one's way
through tears."

English Proverb

"Why comes temptation but
for man to meet
And master and make crouch
beneath his foot,
And so be pedestalled in
triumph?"

Robert Browning

"I can resist everything except
temptation."

Oscar Wilde: Lady Windermere's Fan

"Our life is what our thoughts make it."

Marcus Aurelius

Addresses • Addresses • Addresses • Addresses • Addresses • Addresses • Addresses • Addresses

Name

✉

☎

Name

✉

☎

Name

✉

☎

Name

✉

☎

Name

✉

☎

Name

✉

☎

pop a couple of lumps of sugar into it to prevent mouldy smells developing.

THREAD

To prevent your double thread tangling when sewing, knot the ends separately instead of together.

TOILET BOWLS

You can easily remove hard water marks inside the toilet bowl by pouring three teacups of vinegar into the bowl and allowing it to soak for a few hours before brushing and flushing.

VACUUM FLASK

When storing a vacuum flask empty, leave the top off to avoid getting a musty smell.

If the flask does smell musty, fill it with a mixture of warm water and two tablespoons of white vinegar, leaving it to stand for several minutes before shaking and rinsing well. If this fails to eliminate the smell, try a mixture of hot water and one and a half tablespoons of bicarbonate of soda. Leave it for at least four hours and rinse well.

WALLPAPER

When storing your rolls of wallpaper, keep them horizontal, not upright as the ends are more likely to get damaged if they are left standing up.

WASHING

To prevent dark clothes from picking up fluff when washing them with other items, turn them inside out before placing them in the washing machine.

WASHING-UP LIQUID BOTTLE

A clean washing-up liquid bottle filled with water is an ideal watering can for your house plants, enabling you to control the water and to avoid spillages.

WASTE-DISPOSAL UNIT

To clean your waste disposal unit, sprinkle a dozen or so ice cubes with scouring powder and pass them through it, finishing with a few orange or lemon peels.

WATCHES

If the glass of your watch gets misted up, turn it over and wear the glass next to your skin for a little while. The warmth from your skin will help to clear the mist.

WATERING PLANTS

If you are going away on holiday and can find no one to water your plants, keep them moist by soaking the soil thoroughly and then placing the plant and pot, still dripping, in a polythene bag. Close the bag tightly and place in a position where the plant will receive indirect sunlight.

WEIGHT

When you are keeping an eye on your weight, weigh yourself at the same time of the day once a week. This will give you a truer idea of any weight loss or gain by counteracting any daily fluctuations.

WINDOWS

When painting window frames, protect the glass from paint by laying strips of dampened newspaper along the edges and in the corners. These will be easy to remove afterwards.

EVERYDAY THOUGHTS
for everyday living

"Human thought, like God, makes the
world in its own image."

Adam Clayton Powell

"Nimble thought can jump both
sea and land."

Shakespeare: Sonnets

"Tolerance implies no lack of
commitment to one's own beliefs.
Rather it condemns the oppression of
persecution of others."

J F Kennedy

"The heaviest baggage for a
traveller is an empty purse."

English Proverb

"In travelling: a man must carry
knowledge with him, if he would
bring home knowledge."

Samuel Johnson

Addresses • Addresses • Addresses • Addresses • Addresses • Addresses • Addresses • Addresses

𝕿

Name
✉

☎
Name
✉

☎
Name
✉

☎
Name
✉

☎
Name
✉

☎
Name
✉

☎
Name
✉

☎

HANDY HINTS

WOOL
Thick wool can be difficult to thread - if you damp it with saliva it tends to just bounce back. Instead, try rolling the tip on a wet piece of soap and then rub it between your fingers. The ply should then stick together.

WRINKLES IN CLOTHES
If you do not have access to an iron, for example if you are travelling, hang the clothes in the bathroom and fill the bath with hot water. If you close the door and leave for a while, the steam should help remove the creases from your garments.

ZIPS
A zip can be helped to run smoothly by rubbing it with a little soft soap, some candle wax or a pencil lead.

MY OWN NOTES

EVERYDAY THOUGHTS
for everyday living

"Uncertainty is the worst of all evils
until the moment when reality makes
us regret uncertainty."

Alphonse Karr

"All uncertainty is fruitful . . . so
long as it is accompanied by the
wish to understand."

Antonio Machado

"Understanding is the beginning
of approving."

André Gide

"In what we really understand we
reason but little."

William Hazlitt

"Between our birth and death we may
touch understanding as a moth
brushes a window with its wing."

Christopher Fry

Addresses • Addresses • Addresses • Addresses • Addresses • Addresses

𝔘

Name
✉

☎

Name
✉

☎

Name
✉

☎

Name
✉

☎

Name
✉

☎

Name
✉

☎

~ PASSENGER TRAIN SERVICE INFORMATION ~

LONDON AREA ENQUIRIES ☎

For Train Services to:

W Yorkshire, N E England, East Coast to Scotland	071-278 2477
Midlands, N Wales, N W England, West Coast to Scotland	071-387 7070
W of England, S Midlands, S Wales	071-262 6767
Gatwick Airport	071-928 2113
Southern England, East Anglia	071-928 5100
Continental Enquiries	071-834 0892
Reservations/Tickets	071-828 0892

INTERCITY SERVICES FROM: ☎

Birmingham	021-643 2711
Bristol	0272 294255
Cardiff	0222 228000
Edinburgh	031-556 2451
Glasgow	041-204 2844
Leeds	0532 448133
Liverpool	051-709 9696
London	071-928 5100
Manchester	061-832 8353
Newcastle	091-232 6262
Sheffield	0742 726411
York	0904 642155

~ DISTANCES IN MILES ~

```
            London
Aberdeen     501  Aberdeen
Birmingham   111  409  Birmingham
Bristol      114  490   82  Bristol
Cardiff      155  492  101   44  Cardiff
Carlisle     301  217  192  273  275  Carlisle
Dover         73  574  184  195  239  374  Dover
Edinburgh    378  123  286  367  365   94  451  Edinburgh
Fishguard    262  494  176  156  112  276  335  383  Fishguard
Fort William 508  158  399  480  482  207  581  145  483  Fort William
Glasgow      394  150  285  366  378   93  467   45  369  114  Glasgow
Holyhead     261  430  153  211  212  212  334  304  169  417  303  Holyhead
Hull         168  348  143  226  244  155  251  225  285  362  250  217  Hull
Inverness    537  105  445  528  524  253  601  159  529   66  176  463  382  Inverness
Leeds        190  322  111  206  212  115  299  229  322  210  163   56  358  Leeds
Liverpool    205  334   94  164  164  116  278  210  160  323  211   93  122  376   74  Liverpool
Manchester   192  332   81  167  172  115  265  209  189  322  210  123   94  375   40   34  Manchester
Newcastle    271  230  209  295  310   58  344  107  326  257  143  260  118  266   92  157  132  Newcastle
Norwich      107  487  155  221  237  287  169  364  331  494  380  299  149  523  174  224  190  257  Norwich
Nottingham   123  388   50  132  152  185  196  265  210  392  278  172   92  424   72  104   74  158  123  Nottingham
Oxford        56  464   62   66  107  256  129  341  207  461  340  202  163  507  169  156  143  256  139   97  Oxford
Penzance     282  683  268  186  230  466  354  560  342  673  559  397  412  720  381  350  353  481  389  318  250  Penzance
Southampton   79  530  128   75  119  322  149  416  231  520  415  283  256  575  235  222  202  322  186  163   66  222  Southampton
```

```
Antrim        17  271  112  189  280   22  213   60  139  125  216  Antrim
Belfast      265  104  195  279   21  212   77  138  129  208  Belfast
Cork         161  125   54  286   62  280  155  202   75  Cork
Dublin       133  189  125  122  149   97  134  104  Dublin
Galway       130  216   63  172   50   84  141  Galway
Killarney    300   67  291  160  211  119  Killarney
Larne        233   77  159  150  229  Larne
Limerick     224   93  144   78  Limerick
Londonderry  131   88  241  Londonderry
Roscommon     51  125  Roscommon
Sligo        176  Sligo
Waterford
```

EVERYDAY THOUGHTS
for everyday living

"To understand all is to pardon all."
[Tout comprendre rend très indulgent.]

Anna Louise de Stael

"A man should always consider how
much he has more than he wants, and
how much more unhappy he might be
than he really is."

Joseph Addison

"When spiders' webs unite, they
can tie up a lion."

Ethiopian Proverb

"Not vain the weakest, if their
force unite."

Homer

"Once men are caught up in an event
they cease to be afraid. Only the
unknown frightens men."

Saint-Exupéry

Addresses • Addresses • Addresses • Addresses • Addresses • Addresses • Addresses

𝔘

Name
✉

☎
Name
✉

☎
Name
✉

☎
Name
✉

☎
Name
✉

☎
Name
✉

☎

TRAVEL INFORMATION

Tyre Pressures									Speed									
lb per sq in	20	22	24	26	28	30	32	34	M.P.H.	20	30	40	50	60	70	80	90	100
kg per sq cm	1.40	1.54	1.68	1.82	1.96	2.10	2.24	2.39	Km.P.H.	32	48	64	80	96	112	128	144	160

Fuel						Distance					
Gallons	1	2	3	4	5	Miles	1	5	10	25	30
Litres	4.55	9.09	13.64	18.18	22.73	Kilometres	1.61	8.05	16.09	40.23	80.47
Gallons	6	7	8	9	10	Miles		75	100	250	500
Litres	27.28	31.82	36.37	40.91	45.46	Kilometres		120.70	160.90	402.27	804.70

~ COACH TRAVEL ~

TRAVEL ENQUIRIES ☎

Victoria Coach Station	071 730 0202
Eastern Scottish Omnibuses	031 556 8464
Scottish Citylink	041 332 9191
Northern Scottish Omnibuses	0224 212266
Birmingham	021 622 4373
Brighton	0273 206666
Cardiff	0222 371331
Cheltenham	0242 584111
Fareham	0329 230023
Leeds	0532 460011
Liverpool	051 709 6481
London	071 730 0202
Manchester	061 228 3881
Newcastle	091 261 6077
Plymouth	0752 671121
Sheffield	0742 754905

~ FERRY TRAVEL ~

TRAVEL ENQUIRIES ☎

Brittany Ferries	0705 827701
Hover Speed Ltd	0304 240101
Advance Bookings	0304 240241
Sally Line Ltd	0843 595566
Sealink UK Ltd	0233 647047
P&O Ferries	0304 203388

~ ROAD & RAIL ~

TRAVEL ENQUIRIES ☎

AA	0345 500 600
RAC	081 686 2314
London Regional Transport (Bus & Tube)	071 222 1234

~ CAR REGISTRATIONS ~

SUFFIX LETTERS						PREFIX LETTERS				
Aug '73 - July '74	M	Aug '78 - July '79	T	A	Aug '83 - July '84	F	Aug '88 - July '89			
Aug '74 - July '75	N	Aug '79 - July '80	V	B	Aug '84 - July '85	G	Aug '89 - July '90			
Aug '75 - July '76	P	Aug '80 - July '81	W	C	Aug '85 - July '86	H	Aug '90 - July '91			
Aug '76 - July '77	R	Aug '81 - July '82	X	D	Aug '86 - July '87	J	Aug '91 - July '92			
Aug '77 - July '78	S	Aug '82 - July '83	Y	E	Aug '87 - July '88	K	Aug '92 - July '93			

EVERYDAY THOUGHTS
for everyday living

"It's not hard to make decisions when you know what your values are."

Roy Disney

"There are no grades of vanity, there are only grades of ability in concealing it."

Mark Twain

"The object of a good general is not to fight, but to win. He has fought enough if he gains a victory."

The Duke of Alva

"Virtue is never left to stand alone. He who has it will have neighbours."

Confucius

"Virtue is the roughest way, But proves at night a bed of down."

Sir Henry Wotton

Addresses • Addresses • Addresses • Addresses • Addresses • Addresses • Addresses • Addresses

Name

✉

☎

Name

✉

☎

Name

✉

☎

Name

✉

☎

Name

✉

☎

Name

✉

☎

Name

✉

☎

TRAVEL PROTECTION

DISEASE	RISK AREAS	HOW CAUGHT	VACCINATION	CERTIFICATE
CHOLERA	Africa, Asia, Middle East, especially in conditions of poor hygiene and sanitation	From contaminated food or water	Usually 2 injections by your doctor. Certificate valid for 6 months	Some countries may require evidence of vaccination within previous 6 months
VIRAL HEPATITIS A	Most parts of the world but especially in conditions of poor hygiene and sanitation	From contaminated food or water	Immunoglobulin if not already immune	No
VIRAL HEPATITIS B	World-wide	By intimate contact with an infected person; from injections with infected blood or needles	Your doctor will advise on the need for vaccination	No
MALARIA	Africa, Asia, Central and South America	Bite from infected mosquito	None, but anti-malarial tablets are available	No
POLIOMYELITIS	Everywhere except Australia, New Zealand, Europe and North America	Direct contact with an infected person; rarely by contaminated water or food	Drops by mouth in 3 doses (spacing depends upon age). Reinforcing dose advised after 3 years	No
RABIES	Many parts of the world	Bite or scratch from an infected animal	Vaccination may be advised after a bite. Get advice from a doctor immediately	No
TETANUS	World-wide but particularly dangerous in places where medical facilities are not readily available	Any skin-penetrating wound, especially if soiled	Vaccination is safe, effective and gives long-lasting protection	No
TUBERCULOSIS	Asia, Africa, Central and South America	Airborne from infectious person	Skin test and injection at least 2 months before travel	No
TYPHOID	Everywhere except Australia, New Zealand, Europe and North America in conditions of poor hygiene and bad sanitation	Contaminated food, water or milk	2 injections from your doctor, 4-6 weeks apart. Revaccination by 1 injection usually after 3 years	No
YELLOW FEVER	Africa and South America	Bite from infected mosquito	1 injection at a yellow-fever vaccination centre at least 10 days before you go. Certificate valid for 10 years	Yes Valid 10 years Greece requires a certificate if recently visited risk areas

VISITING EUROPE

To get emergency medical help in most European Community countries you will need a form E111, available from the Post Office.

Your E111 will be valid during short visits abroad as long as you continue to live in the UK. You will need to apply for a new form if you use or hand in the one you hold.

The Department of Health produces two travel information leaflets. T2 is for the EC and is only available from your post office. T3 is for outside the EC and is available from your travel agent and doctor.

EVERYDAY THOUGHTS
for everyday living

"Mankind must put an end to war or war will put an end to mankind."

J F Kennedy

"There never was a good war or a bad peace."

Benjamin Franklin

"Wealthy people miss one of life's great thrills - making the last car payment."

Author Unidentified

"You are as welcome as the flowers in May."

Charles Macklin

"The wisest man sometimes acts weakly, and the weakest sometimes wisely."

Lord Chesterfield

"Wisdom is always an overmatch for strength."

Phaedrus

𝔚

Name

✉

☎

Name

✉

☎

Name

✉

☎

Name

✉

☎

Name

✉

☎

Name

✉

☎

Name

✉

☎

INTERNATIONAL INFORMATION

Country	Capital	Currency	Approx Air Distance from London	GMT	Dial Codes From	To
Australia	Canberra	Dollar	10563	+10	0011	61
Austria	Vienna	Schilling	790	+1	00	43
Belgium	Brussels	Franc	217	+1	00	32
Canada	Ottawa	Dollar	3321	-5	011	1
Denmark	Copenhagen	Kroner	608	+1	009	45
Finland	Helsinki	Markka	1147	+2	990	358
France	Paris	Franc	215	+1	19	33
Germany	Bonn (Berlin)	D. Mark	320	+1	00	49
Hong Kong	Victoria	Dollar	5990	+8	106	852
Hungary	Budapest	Forint	923	+1	00	36
India	New Delhi	Rupee	4180	+5.5	900	91
Ireland (Rep)	Dublin	Irish Pound	279	GMT	16	353
Italy	Rome	Lire	895	+1	00	39
Japan	Tokyo	Yen	5956	+9	001	81
Luxembourg	Luxembourg	Lux'g Franc	310	+1	00	352
Malta	Valletta	Lira	1305	+1	0	356
Netherlands	Amsterdam	Guilder	230	+1	09	31
New Zealand	Wellington	Dollar	11692	+12	00	64
Norway	Oslo	Kroner	723	+1	095	47
Pakistan	Islamabad	P. Rupee	3767	+5	00	92
Poland	Warsaw	Zloty	912	+1	00	48
Portugal	Lisbon	Escudo	972	GMT	07	351
Spain	Madrid	Peseta	773	+1	07	34
Sweden	Stockholm	Kroner	908	+1	009	46
Switzerland	Berne	Franc	476	+1	00	41
USA	Washington DC	Dollar	3665	-5	011	1
Russia	Moscow	Rouble	1557	+3	810	7
Yugoslavia	Belgrade	Y. Dinar	1056	+1	99	38

EVERYDAY THOUGHTS
for everyday living

"The seat of knowledge is in the
head; of wisdom, in the heart.
We are sure to judge wrong if we do
not feel right."

William Hazlitt

"It is easier to be wise on behalf of
others than to be so for ourselves."

La Rochefoucauld

"The growth of wisdom may be gauged
exactly by the dimunition of ill-temper."

Nietzsche

"I never did anything worth doing by
accident, nor did any of my
inventions come by accident; they
came by work."

Thomas A. Edison

"The biggest mistake you can make
is to believe that you work for
someone else."

Author Unidentified

Addresses • Addresses • Addresses • Addresses • Addresses • Addresses • Addresses

Name

✉

☎

Name

✉

☎

Name

✉

☎

Name

✉

☎

Name

✉

☎

Name

✉

☎

𝔚

EUROPE WITHOUT FRONTIERS

The European Economic Community (now known as the European Community as it moves further from a purely economic union) was founded in 1957 by the six countries making up the European Coal and Steel Community: France, Germany (then West Germany), Italy and the Benelux group (Belgium, Luxembourg and the Netherlands). Denmark, Ireland (Eire) and the United Kingdom joined the Community in January of 1973 and have since been joined by Greece in 1981, and most recently by Spain and Portugal in 1986.

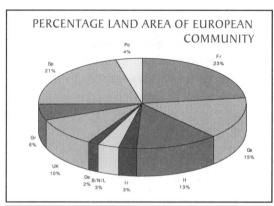

PERCENTAGE LAND AREA OF EUROPEAN COMMUNITY

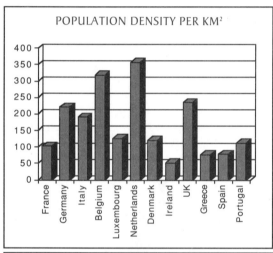

POPULATION DENSITY PER KM²

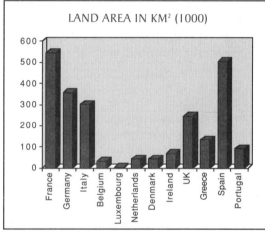

LAND AREA IN KM² (1000)

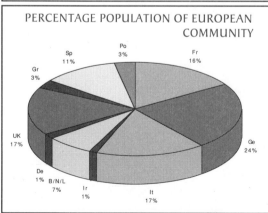

PERCENTAGE POPULATION OF EUROPEAN COMMUNITY

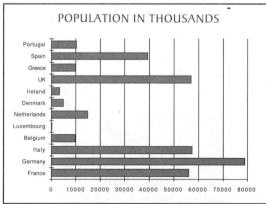

POPULATION IN THOUSANDS

EVERYDAY THOUGHTS
for everyday living

"Our youth we can have but to-day,
We may always find time to grow old."

George Berkeley

"Youth is a fire, and the years are
a pack of wolves who grow
bolder as the fire dies down."

Author Unidentified

"It is better to waste one's youth
than to do nothing with it at all."

Georges Courteline

"Experience shows that success is due
less to ability than to zeal. The winner
is he who gives himself to his work,
body and soul."

Charles Buxton

"Zeal will do more than knowledge."

William Hazlitt

Addresses • Addresses • Addresses • Addresses • Addresses • Addresses • Addresses • Addresses

𝔛
𝔜
𝔃

Name

✉

☎

Name

✉

☎

Name

✉

☎

Name

✉

☎

Name

✉

☎

Name

✉

☎

Name

✉

☎

EUROPE WITHOUT FRONTIERS

BELGIUM

Capital	Brussels
Population	9.88 million
Form of Government	Kingdom
Language(s) Spoken	French, Flemish & German
Currency	Belgian Franc
Area	30,518 km²

Production

Principal Agriculture	Potatoes, Wheat, Barley, Apples
Principal Livestock	Pigs, Cattle
Principal Minerals	Coal, Uranium

Public holidays

New Year	National Holiday (July)
Easter Monday	Assumption
Labour Day	All Saints
Ascension Day	Armistice Day
Whit Monday	Christmas Day

Time

GMT+1	EST+6	late Sept	-	March
GMT+2	EST+7	late March	-	Sept

Business hours
Banks   9 am - 3.30/4 pm Mon-Fri (Brussels city banks)
            9 am - 4 pm Mon-Fri (Antwerp city banks)
            Other banks close for lunch.
Offices   8.30/9 am - 12/12.30 pm and
            2/2.30 - 5.30/6 pm Mon-Fri

International airports
Brussels: Brussels Nat'l Airport, Zaventem 8 miles (13 km)
Antwerp: Deurne 3.4 miles (5.5 km)
Liège: Bierset 5 miles (8 km)

Tourist information
Tourisme information Bruxelles,
Hotel de Ville, Grand' Place,
Brussels 1000   Tel 513 8940

Dialling-
in code
(country)
32

DENMARK

Capital	Copenhagen
Population	5.14 million
Form of Government	Kindom
Language(s) Spoken	Danish
Currency	Danish Krone
Area	43,075 km²

Production

Principal Agriculture	Barley, Wheat, Potatoes, Rape seed, Rye, Oats, Apples
Principal Livestock	Pigs, Cattle
Principal Minerals	Natural Gas, Crude Petroleum

Public holidays

New Year	Ascension Day
Maundy Thursday	Whit Monday
Good Friday	Constitution Day (June)
Easter Monday	Christmas Day
General Prayer Day (May)	Boxing Day

Time

GMT+1	EST+6	late Sept	-	March
GMT+2	EST+7	late March	-	Sept

Business hours
Banks   9.30 am - 4 pm Mon-Fri
                               9.30 am - 6 pm Thu
Government offices   9 am - 4.30/5 pm Mon-Fri
Commercial offices   9 am - 5.30 pm Mon-Fri

International airports
Copenhagen: Kastrup 6 miles (10 km)
Aarhus: Tirstrup 25 miles (40 km)

Tourist information
H C Andersen's Boulevard 22A,
DK-1553 København V   Tel (33) 11 13 25

Dialling-in code (country)   45

— JANUARY PLANNER —

1
2
3
4
5
6
7
8
9
10
11
12
13
14
15
16
17
18
19
20
21
22
23
24
25
26
27
28
29
30
31

— FEBUARY PLANNER —

1
2
3
4
5
6
7
8
9
10
11
12
13
14
15
16
17
18
19
20
21
22
23
24
25
26
27
28
(29)

EUROPE WITHOUT FRONTIERS

FRANCE

Capital	Paris
Population	56.18 million
Form of Government	Republic
Language(s) Spoken	French
Currency	French Franc
Area	543,965 km²

Production
Principal Agriculture   Sugarbeet, Wheat, Maize,
                           Grapes, Barley, Potatoes
Principal Livestock   Cattle, Pigs, Sheep, Horses
Principal Minerals   Salt, Crude Petroleum,
                           Uranium, Potash, Bauxite,

Public holidays   Whit Monday
New Year   National Day (July)
Easter Monday   Assumption
Labour Day   All Saints
Victory Day (May)   Armistice Day
Ascension Day   Christmas Day

Time
GMT+1   EST+6   late Sept   - March
GMT+2   EST+7   late March - Sept

Business hours
Banks   9 am - 4 pm Mon-Fri
                           Many banks are open until 6.30-7 pm
                           and on Sat until 1 pm.
Government offices   9 am - 6 pm Mon-Fri
Commercial offices   9 am - 12 noon and 2 - 6 pm Mon-Fri

International airports
Paris: Charles de Gaulle (Roissy) 19 miles (30 km)
Orly 9 miles (15 km)   Lyons: Satolas 19 miles (30 km)
Marseille: Marignane 15 miles (25 km)
Nice: Cote D'Azur 4 miles (6 km)

Tourist information
127 Avenue des Champs Elysées
75008 Paris   Tel 47236172

Dialling-
in code
(country)

33

GERMANY

Capital	Berlin (Bonn - Govt)
Population	79.07 million
Form of Government	Federal Republic
Language(s) Spoken	German
Currency	Deutschmark
Area	357,039 km²

Production
Principal Agriculture   Potatoes, Wheat, Barley, Rye,
                           Apples, Oats, Grapes
Principal Livestock   Pigs, Cattle, Sheep
Principal Minerals   Salt, Potash, Natural Gas,
                           Coal, Zinc, Silver

Public holidays   Whit Monday
New Year   Day of Unity (October)
Good Friday   Day of Prayer and
Easter Monday   Repentance (November)
Labour Day   Christmas Day
Ascension Day   Second Christmas Day

Time
GMT+1   EST+6   late Sept   - March
GMT+2   EST+7   late March - Sept

Business hours
Banks   8.30 am - 1 pm and
                           2.30 pm - 4 pm Mon - Fri
                           Open until 5.30 pm Thu.
                           Banks in Bonn close on Fri at 3 pm.
Government offices   8 am - 5 pm Mon-Thu.
                           Close Fri 3.30 pm
Commercial offices   8 am - 6 pm Mon-Fri
                           In some areas closing times vary.

International airports
Berlin: Schonefeld 12 miles (20 km), Tegel 5 miles (8 km)

Tourist information
69 Beethovenstrasse,
6000 Frankfurt-am-Main   Tel (69) 75720

Dialling-in code (country)   49

MARCH PLANNER

1 ....
2 ....
3 ....
4 ....
5 ....
6 ....
7 ....
8 ....
9 ....
10 ....
11 ....
12 ....
13 ....
14 ....
15 ....
16 ....
17 ....
18 ....
19 ....
20 ....
21 ....
22 ....
23 ....
24 ....
25 ....
26 ....
27 ....
28 ....
29 ....
30 ....
31 ....

APRIL PLANNER

1 ....
2 ....
3 ....
4 ....
5 ....
6 ....
7 ....
8 ....
9 ....
10 ....
11 ....
12 ....
13 ....
14 ....
15 ....
16 ....
17 ....
18 ....
19 ....
20 ....
21 ....
22 ....
23 ....
24 ....
25 ....
26 ....
27 ....
28 ....
29 ....
30 ....

EUROPE WITHOUT FRONTIERS

GREECE

Capital	Athens
Population	10.14 million
Form of Government	Republic
Language(s) Spoken	Greek
Currency	Drachma
Area	131,957 km²

Production
Principal Agriculture — Wheat, Tomatoes, Grapes, Olives, Potatoes, Tobacco
Principal Livestock — Sheep, Goats
Principal Minerals — Bauxite, Magnesite, Chrome,

Public holidays
New Year
Epiphany
Clean Monday (March)
Nat'l Ind'pendence Day (Mar)
Easter Friday
Easter Monday

Labour Day
Whit Monday
Assumption
Oxi Day (October)
Christmas Day
Second Christmas Day

N.B. Greek Orthodox Easter is the most important festival in Greece.
No business can be done during the Easter weekend.

Time

GMT+2	EST+7	Winter
GMT+3	EST+8	Summer

Business hours
Banks — 8 am - 2 pm Mon-Fri (flexible)
Government offices — 7.30 am - 1.30 pm Mon-Fri
Commercial offices — 8.30 am - 1.30 pm and 4.30 - 7.30 pm
Shops usually close Mon, Wed, Sat afternoons.
Some take long weekends and close on Sat.

Tourist information
Greek Tourist Office,
2 Amerikis Street,
Athens   Tel 322 3111

Dialling-
in code
(country)

30

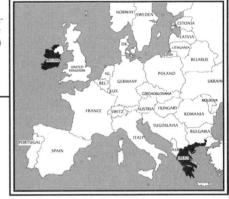

REPUBLIC OF IRELAND

Capital	Dublin
Population	3.54 million
Form of Government	Republic
Language(s) Spoken	Irish, English
Currency	Irish Pound
Area	70,283 km²

Production
Principal Agriculture — Barley, Potatoes, Wheat, Tomatoes, Wool
Principal Livestock — Cattle, Sheep
Principal Minerals — Zinc, Natural Gas, Lead, Silver

Public holidays
New Year
St Patrick's Day (March)
Easter Monday
June Holiday

August Holiday
October Holiday
Christmas Day
St Stephen's Day

N.B. Good Friday is not a public holiday but banks & many businesses close.

Business hours
Commercial/Retail Banks — 10 am - 12.30 pm, 1.30 - 3 pm, Mon-Fri, Thu open until 5 pm
Savings Banks — 10 am - 4 pm Mon-Fri, Thu open until 7 pm
Government offices — 9.15 am - 5.30 pm Mon-Thu, 9.15 am - 5.15 pm Fri
Commercial offices — 9.30 am - 5.30 pm Mon-Fri

International airports
Dublin 5.5 miles (8.8 km)   Cork 5 miles (8 km)
Shannon 16 miles (26 km) from Limerick

Tourist information
14 Upper O'Connell Street, Dublin 1   Tel 747733

Time

GMT	EST+5	late October	-	March
GMT+1	EST+6	late March	-	Oct

Dialing-in code (country)   353

MAY PLANNER

1
2
3
4
5
6
7
8
9
10
11
12
13
14
15
16
17
18
19
20
21
22
23
24
25
26
27
28
29
30
31

JUNE PLANNER

1
2
3
4
5
6
7
8
9
10
11
12
13
14
15
16
17
18
19
20
21
22
23
24
25
26
27
28
29
30

EUROPE WITHOUT FRONTIERS

ITALY

Capital	Rome
Population	57.60 million
Form of Government	Republic
Language(s) Spoken	Italian
Currency	Italian Lira
Area	301,279 km²

Production
Principal Agriculture	Grapes, Wheat, Tomatoes, Maize, Fruits
Principal Livestock	Sheep, Cattle
Principal Minerals	Salt, Natural Gas, Asbestos, Silver, Zinc, Lead

Public holidays
New Year	Assumption (Ferragosto)
Epiphany	All Saints
Easter Sunday	Immaculate Conception
Easter Monday	Christmas Day
Liberation Day (April)	St Stephen's Day

N.B. Business is very much disrupted in the holiday season, mid-July to mid-September, and from December 23 to January 6. Also, local public holidays are celebrated on the feast day of the patron saint of each town.

Time
GMT+1	EST+6	late Sept	-	March
GMT+2	EST+7	late March	-	Sept

Business hours
Banks	8.30 am - 1.20 pm & 3-4 pm Mon-Fri
Government offices	8 am - 2 pm Mon-Sat
Commercial offices	
Northern Italy	8.30 am - 12.45 pm; 3-6.30 pm Mon-Fri
Central &S'n Italy	8.30 am - 12.45 pm; 4.30/5 - 8 pm M-F

International airports
Bari, Bologna, Catania, Florence, Genoa, Milan, Naples, Palermo, Rome, Trieste, Turin, Venice.

Tourist information
Via Marghera 2, 00185 Rome   Tel 49711

Dialling-in code (country)

39

LUXEMBOURG

Capital	Luxembourg
Population	0.38 million
Form of Government	Grand Duchy
Language(s) Spoken	Luxembourgeois, French, German
Currency	Luxembourg Franc
Area	2,586 km²

Production
Principal Livestock	Cattle, Pigs

Public holidays
New Year	National Day (June)
Easter Monday	Assumption
Labour Day	All Saints
Ascension Day	Christmas Day
Whit Monday	St Stephen's Day

N.B. Many businesses close on Carnival Monday in February, All Souls Day in November and on Luxembourg Fair Day in September.

Time
GMT+1	EST+6	late Sept	-	end March
GMT+2	EST+7	late March	-	end Sept

Business hours
Banks	8.30 am - 12 noon, 1.30 pm - 4.30 pm Mon-Fri
Government offices	9 am - 12 noon, 2 pm - 5 pm Mon-Fri
Commercial offices	8 am - 12 noon, 2 pm - 6 pm Mon-Fri

International airport
Luxembourg: Findel 5 miles (7 km)

Tourist information
Place de la Gare
c/o Air Terminal
1616 Luxembourg   Tel 481199

Dialing-in code (country)   352

JULY PLANNER

1
2
3
4
5
6
7
8
9
10
11
12
13
14
15
16
17
18
19
20
21
22
23
24
25
26
27
28
29
30
31

AUGUST PLANNER

1
2
3
4
5
6
7
8
9
10
11
12
13
14
15
16
17
18
19
20
21
22
23
24
25
26
27
28
29
30
31

EUROPE WITHOUT FRONTIERS

NETHERLANDS

Capital	Amsterdam
Population	15 million
Form of Government	Kingdom
Language(s) Spoken	Dutch
Currency	Guilder
Area	41,863 km²

Production
Principal Agriculture   Potatoes, Wheat, Tomatoes,
                             Apples, Barley, Pears

Principal Livestock   Pigs, Cattle
Principal Minerals   Salt, Natural Gas, Crude
                             Petroleum

Public holidays
New Year   Ascension Day
Good Friday   Whit Monday
Easter Monday   Christmas Holiday

N.B. In Roman Catholic regions (North Brabant and Limburg) RC
holidays are sometimes local public holidays. On December 5 (St
Nicholas) many firms close at noon. Many sectors of Dutch industry take
holidays in July or August. Queen's Day (April) and Liberation Day
(May) are public holidays for the Civil Service.

Time
GMT+1   EST+6   end Sept   -   end March
GMT+2   EST+7   end March   -   end Sept

Business hours
Banks   9 am - 4 pm Mon-Fri
Government offices   8.30 am - 5 pm Mon-Fri
Commercial offices   8.30 am - 5.30 pm Mon - Fri

International airports
Amsterdam: Schiphol 9 miles (15 km)
Rotterdam: Zestienhoven 5.5 miles (9 km)
Maastricht: Beek 4.5 miles (8 km)

Tourist information
Stationsplein 10, 1076 CL Amsterdam   Tel 266444

Dialling-
in code
(country)

31

PORTUGAL

Capital	Lisbon
Population	10.35 million
Form of Government	Republic
Language(s) Spoken	Portuguese
Currency	Escudo
Area	92,072 km²

Production
Principal Agriculture   Grapes, Tomatoes, Maize,
                             Wheat, Olives, Wool

Principal Livestock   Sheep, Pigs
Principal Minerals   Tungsten, Silver

Public holidays
New Year   Corpus Christi
Shrove Tuesday   Assumption
Good Friday   Republic Day (October)
Easter Sunday   All Saints
National Day (April)   Independence Day (Dec)
Labour Day   Immaculate Conception
Camoes Day (June)   Christmas Day

N.B. Business visits are not recommended in July, August and September
as most businessmen take their holidays at this time. Banks are closed on
December 26.

Time
GMT   EST+5   late Sept   -   late March
GMT+1   EST+6   late March   -   late Sept

Business hours
Banks   8.30 am - 2.45 pm Mon-Fri
            Certain central branches in Lisbon also open
            6 - 11 pm Mon-Fri
Offices   9 am - 1 pm and 3 - 6 pm Mon-Fri

International airports
Lisbon: Portela de Sacavem 6.5 miles (10 km)
Oporto 8 miles (13 km)   Faro 4.5 miles (7 km)

Tourist information
Praca dos Restauradores, Lisbon   Tel 367031

Dialing-in code (country)   351

SEPTEMBER PLANNER

1
2
3
4
5
6
7
8
9
10
11
12
13
14
15
16
17
18
19
20
21
22
23
24
25
26
27
28
29
30

OCTOBER PLANNER

1
2
3
4
5
6
7
8
9
10
11
12
13
14
15
16
17
18
19
20
21
22
23
24
25
26
27
28
29
30
31

EUROPE WITHOUT FRONTIERS

SPAIN

Capital	Madrid
Population	39.54 million
Form of Government	Monarchy
Language(s) Spoken	Spanish
Currency	Spanish Peseta
Area	504,750 km²

Production
Principal Agriculture	Barley, Grapes, Wheat, Olives, Tomatoes, Oranges
Principal Livestock	Sheep
Principal Minerals	Pigs

Public holidays
New Year	St James the Apostle (July)
Epiphany	Assumption
St Joseph's Day (March)	National Day (October)
Holy Thursday	All Saints Day
Good Friday	Constitution Day (December)
Labour Day	Immaculate Conception
	Christmas Day

N.B. Avoid business visits from July to September.
In addition to public holidays each town and region has its own Fiesta.

Time
GMT+1	EST+6	late Sept - March
GMT+2	EST+7	late March - Sept

Business hours
Office hours vary considerably and business visitors should check with individual firms and banks.

International airports
Madrid 10 miles (16 km)   Barcelona 9 miles (15 km)
Malaga 5 miles (8 km)
Bilbao, Valencia, Alicante, Almeria, Gerona, Santiago.

Tourist information
Duque Medinaceli 2, Madrid   Tel 2211268

Dialling-in code (country)

34

UNITED KINGDOM

Capital	London
Population	57.24 million
Form of Government	Kingdom
Language(s) Spoken	English
Currency	English Pound
Area	244,103 km²

Production
Principal Agriculture	Wheat, Barley, Potatoes, Oats, Apples, Wool
Principal Livestock	Sheep, Cattle
Principal Minerals	Salt, Natural Gas, Crude Petroleum, Coal, Tin

Public holidays
New Year	Spring Holiday (May)
St Patrick's Day (NI) (March)	Holiday (NI) (July)
Good Friday*	Late Summer Holiday (Aug)*
Easter Monday*	Christmas Day
May Day Holiday	Boxing Day*

* Not a public holiday in Scotland - dates differ

Time
GMT	EST+5	Winter (late Oct - late March)
GMT+1	EST+6	Summer (late March - late Oct)

Business hours
Banks	9.15 am - 4.45 pm Mon-Fri
	Open until 5.30 pm Thu
	Certain branches are open Sat morning
Government offices	Variable, Mon-Fri
Commercial offices	9 am - 5 pm/9.30 am - 5.30 pm Mon-Fri

Business information
British Overseas Trade Board,
Fairs and Promotions Branch,
Department of Trade and Industry   Tel 071-215 5000

Dialing-in code (country)   44

NOVEMBER PLANNER

1 ....
2 ....
3 ....
4 ....
5 ....
6 ....
7 ....
8 ....
9 ....
10 ....
11 ....
12 ....
13 ....
14 ....
15 ....
16 ....
17 ....
18 ....
19 ....
20 ....
21 ....
22 ....
23 ....
24 ....
25 ....
26 ....
27 ....
28 ....
29 ....
30 ....

DECEMBER PLANNER

1 ....
2 ....
3 ....
4 ....
5 ....
6 ....
7 ....
8 ....
9 ....
10 ....
11 ....
12 ....
13 ....
14 ....
15 ....
16 ....
17 ....
18 ....
19 ....
20 ....
21 ....
22 ....
23 ....
24 ....
25 ....
26 ....
27 ....
28 ....
29 ....
30 ....
31 ....

Name _____

✉ _____

_____

☎ _____

Name _____

✉ _____

_____

☎ _____

Name _____

✉ _____

_____

☎ _____

Name _____

✉ _____

_____

☎ _____

Name _____

✉ _____

_____

☎ _____

Name _____

✉ _____

_____

☎ _____

Name _____

✉ _____

_____

☎ _____

Name _____

✉ _____

_____

☎ _____

Name _____

✉ _____

_____

☎ _____

Name _____

✉ _____

_____

☎ _____

Name _____

✉ _____

_____

☎ _____

Name _____

✉ _____

_____

☎ _____

Name

✉

☎

Name

✉

☎

Name

✉

☎

Name

✉

☎

Name

✉

☎

Name

✉

☎

Name

✉

☎

Name

✉

☎

Name

✉

☎

Name

✉

☎

Name

✉

☎

Name

✉

☎

Name

✉

☎

Name

✉

☎